一式搞定
狄克生片語

Color Your English with Idioms

一式搞定狄克生片語
Color Your English with Idioms

發 行 人	鄭俊琪
總 編 輯	陳豫弘
副總編輯	李芳田
編　　輯	璩雅琪‧林詩嘉‧徐采薇
作　　者	Stephen Riter‧Steven Tisdale‧李芳田
英文校對	Stephen Riter‧Steven Tisdale
英文錄音	Steven Tisdale
美術設計	鄭賀云
技術總監	李志純
介面設計	曹寶泰
光碟製作	李宛晏‧黃鈺皓‧翁子雲
出版發行	希伯崙股份有限公司
	105台北市松山區八德路3段32號12樓
	劃撥：1939-5400
	電話：(02)2578-7838　傳真：(02)2578-5800
	電子郵件：Service@LiveABC.com
法律顧問	朋博法律事務所
印　　刷	禹利電子分色有限公司
出版日期	民國96年4月　初版三刷
原　　價	書 + 朗讀MP3 + 電腦互動光碟：450元
推 廣 價	書 + 朗讀MP3 + 電腦互動光碟：350元

本書若有缺頁、破損、裝訂錯誤，請寄回本公司更換
版權所有，禁止以任何方式，在任何地方作全部或局部翻印、仿製或轉載
Copyright © 2006 by LiveABC Interactive Corporation
All rights reserved. Printed in Taiwan

一式搞定
狄克生片語

Color Your English with Idioms

英語數位學習第一品牌

編輯的話 Editor's Note

學片語 也學語感

《狄克生片語》對台灣學習英文的人而言，幾乎是必讀的入門工具書，因此市面上相關的書籍可謂為數眾多。只不過，我們發現，經過這許多年，大部分的英文片語書，仍跳脫不了既有的學習框架，讀者還是得靠記憶把這些片語生吞活剝，而無法觸類旁通。因此，我們大膽採用拆解式解說，不放過任何簡單的單字，讓讀者在很短的時間內，迅速理解片語的組成與由來，不再讓片語成為「騙語」──有看沒有懂。

對於初學《狄克生片語》的讀者來說，相信都有過類似的感覺：fall for 為什麼是「迷戀；被騙」，難道迷戀上某人就一定會被騙？stand up 為什麼不是「站上去」？可是怎麼好像在電影裡聽到過 stand me up 是「放我鴿子」？eat in 為什麼是「在家吃」？eat up 怎麼會有「吃光」的意思？老師不是說過代名詞作受詞時，一定要放在片語動詞中間，怎麼會有 turn on you「與你敵對」這個用法？為什麼不能說 check in the hotel 而要說成 check in at the hotel 或 check into the hotel？……對於這許許多多的疑問，難道只能一個一個把它們記起來，別無他法？

當然不是這樣，如果你知道 fall for 是源自魚看到魚餌時，游下去吃魚餌的動作，而引申指「為……而傾心；上鉤」，你就不必再用「迷戀上某人就一定會被騙」來記這個片語，甚至在使用片語時，感覺會變得不一樣，這就是所謂的語感！你會知道 Tony is the last man she'd ever fall for. 意思是「湯尼是她最不可能愛上的男人。」、She falls for his lies again and again. 意思是「她一再被他的謊言所欺騙。」

為讓讀者在學片語時能夠觸類旁通，碰到不會的可自行推敲，本書所有片語皆採拆解式解說，迅速增進你的英文語感。我們僅以第一課的 eat up 為例：

> **解說** eat（吃）＋ up（完成）＝ 吃完；吃掉

運用一個簡單的拆解公式，讓您一次學會該片語，其後還列舉了許多類似的用法：use up（用完）、burn up（燒光）、tie up（捆好）、dress up（盛裝打扮）、cut up（切碎）、break up（打碎）、tear up（撕碎）、chew up（咬碎）、give up（放棄），讓您將片語一串一

串地學起來。學完後,您是不是很容易就能看出 Who ate up my cake? 和 Who ate my cake? 兩者之間的細微差異。

本書每課的學習內容編排如下:

- 我們都知道,片語不分類,讀起來會很累。所以我們將《狄克生片語》分類彙整為三十大主題,讓讀者在學習時有所依歸。
- 每個主題以一短文開始,讓讀者從文章中活學活用《狄克生片語》。
- 所有片語皆採拆解式解說,讓讀者清楚知道片語的組成與由來,並附有例句、中譯、註解、活用句型公式、相關用語等,讓您從此不再用錯片語。

以下是其中標註代號的對照表:

【解說】:解釋說明	【似】:相似詞	【註】:註解
【例】:例句	【衍】:衍生詞	【可分開片語】:受詞可放片語中間或後面
【同】:同義詞	【聯】:相關用語	
【反】:反義詞	【比】:易混淆	

- 書後的精彩附錄,將新、舊版《狄克生片語》彙整分為三十大主題,並依照各主題之英文字母順序排列,以方便讀者參照、查詢,增進學習效果。
- 本書最後還附有背誦卡,方便讀者隨身攜帶學習。

老實說,《狄克生片語》並非本書學習的終極目標,它只是我們幫讀者練功、培養語感的工具,希望讀者能利用在本書所學到的技巧,迅速學會並掌握更多片語的正確用法,在英語學習的路上走得更順遂。

Contents

編輯的話　　　　　　　　　　　　　　　　　　　　　4

目錄　　　　　　　　　　　　　　　　　　　　　　　6

Lesson 1　Eating 飲食　`Track 1`　　　　　　　　　11
- eat in/out • wait on • dish out • help yourself
- eat up • taste of • throw up • clean up
- pick up the tab • go Dutch

Lesson 2　Dressing 服飾穿著　`Track 2`　　　　　　19
- wear out • dress up • inside out • up to date
- take off • try on • take in • pick out
- put on • be in/out

Lesson 3　Family Life 居家生活　`Track 3`　　　　　29
- stay in/out • stop by • get used to • bring up
- call on • clean out • put away • get up
- see off • make up

Lesson 4　Driving 開車　`Track 4`　　　　　　　　37
- get lost • drop off • drive up to • make room for
- get in • back up • get on • slow down
- run over • run into

Lesson 5　Trips 旅遊　`Track 5`　　　　　　　　　45
- look forward to • goof off • set out • line up
- check in/out • take it easy • work out • take (time) off
- take part (in) • have a good time

Lesson 6　Learning 學習　`Track 6`　　　　　　　53
- major in • stay up • read over • by heart
- hand in • figure out • learn the ropes • call the roll
- look up • lose one's touch

Lesson 7　Health 健康　`Track 7`　　　　　　　　　　61
- get tired • under the weather • look after • build up
- catch cold • get over • put on weight • get sick
- send for • pass out

Lesson 8　Explanation 解釋說明　`Track 8`　　　　　69
- according to • account for • as for • point out
- for example • get through to • in terms of • nothing but
- on the other hand • let alone

Lesson 9　Advice 建議　`Track 9`　　　　　　　　　77
- come true • fall through • hold good • get the better of
- screw up • in vain • at stake • carry out
- give up • give in

Lesson 10　Time 時間　`Track 10`　　　　　　　　85
- from now on • all day long • so far • on time
- for the time being • right away • for good • waste time over
- day after day • take one's time

Lesson 11　Frequency 頻率　`Track 11`　　　　　　93
- as soon as • at times • every now and then • all along
- stand a chance • every other • for once • off and on
- time and again • once in a blue moon

Lesson 12　Order 順序　`Track 12`　　　　　　　101
- sooner or later • one after another • take turns • mix up
- about to • all of a sudden • at first • before long
- at last • in the long run

Lesson 13　Cause & Effect 因果關係　`Track 13`　　109
- ask for • as a result • turn out • have to do with
- now that • lead to • in fact • take place
- break out • no wonder

Lesson 14   Wealth 財富   Track 14   117
• a steal • cut corners • live it up • buy up
• sell out • be well-off • earn a living • get out from under
• be better off • trade in

Lesson 15   Contacting 接洽聯絡   Track 15   125
• kick around • get in touch with • call up • hang up
• hold on • talk over • cut in • by the way
• leave open • be in (someone's) shoes

Lesson 16   Argument 爭執   Track 16   133
• speak ill of • give (someone) a break • beat around the bush
• hear of • find fault with • back out • clear up • call down
• talk back to • search me

Lesson 17   On the Job 工作   Track 17   141
• cover for • be cut out for • on duty • take over
• let slide • carry on • set up • stand for
• lay off • call it a day

Lesson 18   Situations 狀況   Track 18   149
• on the whole • be bound to • stand out • thanks to
• all in all • as usual • be looking up • turn around
• close call • last straw

Lesson 19   Extent 程度   Track 19   157
• go around • at least • by no means • at all
• by far • in addition to • more or less • at best
• run out of • sum up

Lesson 20   Reactions 反應   Track 20   165
• have one's way • look down on • get carried away • show off
• take for granted • play up to • put up with • once and for all
• keep one's head • make believe

Lesson 21   Support 支持   Track 21   173
- live up to • out of the question • draw the line at • by all means
- turn down • keep one's fingers crossed • see eye to eye
- take at one's word • stand up for • give (someone) a big hand

Lesson 22   Relationships 關係   Track 22   181
- give and take • get along with • come across • fall for
- let on • take care of • make up with • break off
- hear from • fool around

Lesson 23   Making Arrangements 安排   Track 23   189
- set out to • think over • take into account • rule out
- in advance • feel like • on the ball • have in mind
- in case • it figures

Lesson 24   Movement 動作   Track 24   197
- keep up with • make good time • dry run • pick up
- take hold of • back and forth • turn on • stick around
- hold still • rise to one's feet

Lesson 25   Obstacles 阻礙   Track 25   205
- out of order • get rid of • prevent from • but for
- go over • go wrong • check up on • interfere with
- be in the/one's way • make waves

Lesson 26   Paying Attention 警覺   Track 26   213
- on one's toes • in a hurry • pay attention (to) • keep an eye on
- turn up • take by surprise • keep track of • look for
- look out • see about

Lesson 27   Differences 判別   Track 27   221
- be a far cry from • all the same • know by sight • take after
- at the sight of • cut down on • look into • tell from
- look over • take for

Lesson 28 In Charge 管控   `Track 28`   229
- make use of • play by ear • get away with • be in charge of
- count on • take pains • make do • meet (someone) halfway
- take up • in hand

Lesson 29 Scheduling 時程   `Track 29`   237
- fall behind • catch up • little by little • a lost cause
- do without • do away with • put off • in time
- on schedule • hold over

Lesson 30 Crimes 犯罪   `Track 30`   245
- hold up • break into • blow up • set fire to
- burn down • let go (of) • tear up • put out
- put down • get even with

....

翻譯 & 測驗解答   252

附錄   278

背誦卡   289

Lesson 1

飲食 Eating

Track 1

My father always told me, "Girlfriends always want to eat out;[1] wives always want to eat in."[1] I wanted a girlfriend. Her name was Wanda. So, I asked her to a candlelit dinner.

At the restaurant, when the guy waiting on[2] us brought our food, I tried to dish it out[3] for Wanda. But Wanda said she'd help herself[4] and ate the food up.[5]

Wanda was a very modern girl. I wanted to show Wanda I was modern, too.

But something happened. With her mouth full, Wanda suddenly looked at me and said, "This food tastes of[6] meat." Wanda said she didn't eat meat. She felt like throwing up.[7]

I guess modern girls don't eat meat.

The waiter cleaned up.[8] Then he brought the check. I had one last chance to show Wanda I was modern, so I suggested she pick up the tab.[9] That made her pretty angry. Then I suggested we go Dutch.[10]

I thought that was fair and equal because I only ate half the food.

She never talked to me again.

❶ eat in/out　在家吃／在外面吃

eat（吃）＋
- in（在家）＝ 在家吃
- out（在外面）＝ 在外面吃

解說　in 和 out 在此皆為副詞，用來表明用餐的方式，其後不必加受詞。
但若當作一般介詞使用，則意思便有所不同，請比較以下兩個例句：

- We decided to eat in a restaurant.　（in 為介系詞，指「在裡面」。）
- We decided to eat in.　（in 為副詞，指「在家」。）

例
- Let's eat in tonight.
  我們今晚就在家吃吧！
- I don't do much cooking; I prefer to eat out.
  我不常做菜，我比較喜歡出去吃。

同　eat in = eat at home = dine in
eat out = go out to eat = eat at a restaurant = dine out

註　eat in/out 和 dine in/out 雖可替代使用，但 dine in/out 屬於正式用語，通常指吃晚餐或大餐，因此在平常會話中使用的機會比 eat in/out 來得低。

❷ wait on　服侍；接待

wait（服務）＋ on（對……）＝ 服侍；接待

解說　wait 在此是指「服務；服侍」，常以 wait on someone 的句型出現，可指「服侍（某人）」或「在餐廳當服務生」，而 wait on (someone) hand and foot 則指「無微不至地照顧（某人）」。

| 飲食 Eating

例 • That rich man has twenty servants waiting on him.
那個富翁有二十個僕人伺候他。

似 wait tables 在餐廳當服務生

❸ dish out　分裝；分配　(可分開片語)

dish（以盤子盛裝）＋ **out**（向外）＝ 盛食物給……

解說　實際上，這個片語時並不限定食物一定要裝在盤子裡，意思相當於 to serve food to people（盛食物給人享用）。

例 • Mom, could you dish out the potatoes for me, please?
媽，麻煩幫我盛些馬鈴薯，好嗎？

似 **dish up** 上菜。
• Come to the table everybody—I'm ready to dish up.
大家到飯桌坐，我準備要上菜了。

衍 **dish it out** 辱罵；斥責
• Somebody can dish it out but they can't take it.
有些人喜歡斥責別人，但自己卻不願受人批評。

❹ help yourself　自行取用

help（取用）＋ **yourself**（你自己）＝ 自行取用

解說　help 在這裡並不是指「幫助」，而是用餐時的招呼語，也就是幫別人「夾」菜、

Lesson 1

「取用」食物。常以「help yourself + to + 事物」句型出現。

例
- Please feel free to help yourself to coffee or tea.
  請自行取用咖啡或茶。

可分開片語

❺ eat up　吃完；吃掉

eat（吃）+ **up**（完成）= 吃完；吃掉

解說　副詞 up 除作「上升」、「起來」解外，亦常有「完成；徹底」的意思。舉例來說，use（使用）+ up（完）= 用完，以下我們再多舉些例子，好讓讀者能更熟悉 up 的用法：

eat up	吃光
burn up	燒光
tie up	捆好
dress up	盛裝
cut up	切碎
break up	打碎
tear up	撕碎
chew up	咬碎
give up	放棄

比
- Who ate up my cake? 誰吃掉我的蛋糕？

- Who ate my cake? 誰吃了我的蛋糕？

| 註 | eat up 也可以用來催促別人「趕快吃」。

- Kids, stop talking now and eat up.
  孩子們，現在別說話，快吃！

---

❻ taste of　嚐起來有……的味道

taste（品嚐）＋ **of**（具有……的）＝ 嚐起來有……的味道

| 解說 | taste 作動詞用，後面的「of ＋ 名詞」是指「有……的味道」，當然，你也可以說某物 taste like（嚐起來像……）。同樣地，某物「聞起來有……的味道」或「聞起來像……」便可說成：smell of、smell like。

| 例 |
- The bread tastes of strawberries.
  這麵包有草莓的味道。

---

❼ throw up　嘔吐

throw（投擲）＋ **up**（向上）＝ 向上拋

| 解說 | throw up 是個口語用法，指的是將胃裡的東西向上從嘴巴吐出來。

| 例 |
- Mary felt sick and started to throw up after eating the spoiled food.
  吃到腐敗的食物後，瑪麗覺得作嘔，並開始嘔吐。

| 同 | **vomit** 是「嘔吐」的正式用語。

Lesson 1

聯　暈機時用的嘔吐袋叫作 airsickness bag。

❽ clean up　清理乾淨；梳洗一下　（可分開片語）

clean（清潔）＋ up（徹底）＝ 清理乾淨

解說　clean up 一般是指「打掃除去（污染物、垃圾等）；清潔（某地方）」，也可以指用餐前的「梳洗」。

但要提醒讀者，clean up 若指用餐前的梳洗，通常只是簡單地洗洗手或臉，並沒有「徹底清潔」的意思。

例
- Give me five minutes to clean myself up before we go out to dinner.
  在我們出去吃晚餐前，給我五分鐘梳洗一下。

❾ pick up the tab　付帳

pick up（拿起）＋ the tab（帳單）＝ 拿起帳單

解說　tab 是個口語用法，指在餐廳、旅館等消費的「帳單」，而 pick up the tab（拿起帳單）即引申指「買單；付帳」。

例
- Jenny picked up the tab when we had dinner together.
  我們一起去吃晚餐，由珍妮買單請客。

同　pick up the bill、pay the bill (付帳)

飲食 Eating

❿ go Dutch　各自付帳

go（處於某種狀態）＋ **Dutch**（荷蘭式的）＝ 採荷蘭式的

解說　Dutch 在此作形容詞用，意思是「荷蘭式的」，至於荷蘭人吃飯時是否習慣各自付帳，並無明確的史料可考。

但可以確定的是，過去荷蘭在歷史上是英國的勁敵，因此 Dutch 這個字常含有輕蔑之意，而 go Dutch 也許就是英國人用來諷刺別人小氣、不請客的代用語吧！

例
- I haven't got enough to pay for all of this; can we go Dutch?
  我不夠錢付全部，我們可以各付各的嗎？

似　split the bill（拆帳各付各的）、Dutch treat（各付各的）

活用狄克生片語 Lesson 1 複習測驗

一、選擇題（請選出一個最適當的選項）

1. I don't want to go to a restaurant tonight, so let's _____.
   (A) eat out   (B) eat in   (C) eat with   (D) eat up

2. No, please don't pay for me; we can _____.
   (A) go Dutch   (B) throw up   (C) wait on   (D) eat up

3. I was very hungry, so I _____ my food really fast.
   (A) ate in   (B) eat in   (C) ate up   (D) eat up

4. I like to treat friends, so I usually _____ the tab when we eat at a restaurant.
   (A) put out   (B) pull out   (C) pick to   (D) pick up

二、翻譯填空

1. 這生日蛋糕嚐起來有香蕉巧克力的味道。
   The birthday cake _____ _____ banana and chocolate.

2. 我喜歡吃媽媽煮的菜，但吃完後卻討厭清理。
   I like eating my mother's food, but I don't like _____ when we finish.

3. 我如果吃太多月餅，就會想吐。
   If I eat too much Moon cake, I'll feel _____ _____.

三、中翻英

1. 農曆過年時，我母親會幫所有家人盛美味可口的湯。

2. 不像中國人的傳統，西方人 (Westerner) 用餐時會要客人自行取用。

3. 中國人很好客（hospitality），常樂於為客人服務。

Lesson 2

服飾穿著 Dressing

Track 2

My boyfriend didn't understand fashion. His pants and shoes were worn out.[1] He didn't like to dress up[2] in nice clothes. When his clothes were dirty, he just turned his clothes inside out[3] and wore them that way.

One day we walked in the city and girls laughed at him. They said he dressed like a chicken farmer.

He didn't care, but I was embarrassed. I decided to bring him up to date.[4]

I took him to fashionable stores. I made him take off[5] his stupid clothes. I asked him to try on[6] cool pants. The pants were too big, so the salesman took them in.[7] They looked perfect.

Then I picked out[8] stylish shoes and colorful shirts. I made him put them on.[9] When I was finished, he was up to date.

My boyfriend said he didn't care. But I cared.

Later, we saw the girls again. This time, they didn't laugh. They smiled. My boyfriend smiled back.

Now things are different. My boyfriend is very in.[10]

Maybe that's why we left the city, moved to the country and started a chicken farm.

Lesson 2

❶ wear out　穿破；穿壞　*可分開片語*

wear（磨損）＋ **out**（完全地）＝ 穿破；穿壞

解說　wear 除指「穿戴」外，亦可指「磨損」，因此 wear out 常指衣服鞋襪等因穿著或使用而「破損不堪使用」。

例
- My shoes are beginning to wear out.
  我的鞋子開始有些破損。

註　但 wear out 如果用來形容人則指「筋疲力竭；極為疲倦」，與 tire out、be exhausted 意思相近。

- I'm worn out.
  我累死了。

- All the hard work quickly wore me out.
  這麼多辛苦的工作很快就讓我筋疲力竭。

---

❷ dress up　盛裝打扮

dress（穿衣）＋ **up**（徹底）＝ 盛裝打扮

解說　dress up 一般譯為「盛裝打扮」，通常是指「穿著比平常更正式的服飾」。例如：Why are you so dressed up today?（你今天為什麼穿得這麼正式？）。

例
- Mary dressed up for her date with Frank.
  瑪莉為了與法蘭克約會而盛裝打扮。

註 dress up 亦可指「打扮成……模樣」，尤其是參加 Halloween party（萬聖節派對），例如：

- Jenny dressed up as a witch for the Halloween party.
  珍妮打扮成巫婆參加萬聖節派對。

【dress 的用法】

dress 當名詞是「衣服；婦女禮服」；當動詞則有「穿衣」的意思，以下是動詞 dress 幾個常見的用法：

be dressed in (something) 穿著（某物）
- Who is that woman dressed in the red skirt?
  那個穿紅裙子的女人是誰？

be dressed to + V. 打扮要……的樣子
- You look like you're dressed to get some exercise.
  你穿得好像是要去作運動。

be dressed to the nines 盛裝打扮
- All of the movie stars were dressed to the nines for the awards ceremony.
  所有的電影明星都盛裝出席頒獎典禮。

---

❸ inside out　內外反過來

inside（內部）＋ **out**（向外）＝ 內外反過來

解說　inside out 指將裡面翻轉到外面，也就是「內外反過來」。

例
- I put my sweater on inside out by mistake.
  我不小心把毛衣給穿反了。

Lesson 2

聯　• upside down 上下顛倒

註　inside out 也有「徹底；完全」的意思，常以 know something inside out 的句型出現，例如：

• Tony knows the system inside out.
　湯尼對這個系統瞭若指掌。

---

❹ up to date　最新

up to（直到）＋ **date**（日期）＝ 到今天為止

解說　up to date 這個片語源自記帳時，必須登錄當天最新的帳目，因此含有「最新」之意。若當形容詞用，要拼成 **up-to-date**。

例
• Bill, long time no see. So, bring me up to date on your life.
　比爾，好久不見。來，告訴我你近況如何。

• Don't use that information; it's not up-to-date.
　別用那則資訊；它不是最新的。

反　out of date 過時的；過期的

---

❺ take off　脫掉　（可分開片語）

take（取得）＋ **off**（離開）＝ 取走；脫掉

解說　take off 是指脫掉身上所穿的衣物、珠寶等。

服飾穿著 **Dressing**

例
- The man took off his shoes before diving into the lake to save the child.
  那名男子脫掉鞋子，跳到湖裡去救那個孩子。

反 put on 穿戴

註 take off 亦可指「（飛機）起飛」，或進而引申表示「（觀念、計畫；產品等）在短時間內迅速獲得大眾喜愛」，但此時卻為不可分動詞，例如：

- That movie really took off among young viewers.
  那部電影大受年輕觀眾歡迎。

❻ try on　試穿　可分開片語

try（嘗試）＋ **on**（在……之上）＝ 試穿；試戴

解說　try on 指試穿或試戴飾品、衣物等。

例
- You should try on that shirt before you buy it.
  你在買那件襯衫之前最好先試穿看看。

似　若是機器設備等的「試用」則要用 try out 表示。

❼ take in　縮小尺寸　可分開片語

take（承擔）＋ **in**（在裡面）＝ 收進到裡面

解說　take in 除指將衣物「改小；縮小尺寸」外，還有以下幾種常見的用法：

1. 縮小尺寸

    I'll have to take this skirt in at the waist—it's too big.
    我必須將這件裙子的腰圍改小,因為太大了。

2. 觀看;參觀(同 watch、attend)

    We're going to get something to eat and then take in a movie.
    我們要去吃點東西,然後看場電影。

3. 了解

    That's too much information for me to take in all at once!
    資料太多了,我沒辦法一下子全部搞懂!

4. 欺騙

    Don't be taken in by the outrageous claims of that sales representative!
    別被那個推銷員天花亂墜的說詞給騙了!

反　let out 放大尺寸

---

❽ pick out　挑選

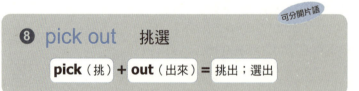

解說　pick out 是指從一群人或一堆事物之中作挑選。

例
- Could you help me pick out some new curtains?
  請幫我挑選一些新的窗簾好嗎?

似　choose、select「選擇;挑選」

服飾穿著 Dressing

❾ put on 穿戴；塗抹   〔可分開片語〕

put（放置）＋ on（在……之上）＝ 穿上；戴上；塗抹

解說 put on 指將衣物等「穿戴」到身上的動作，如果是指穿著的狀態則要用動詞 wear。除了穿衣服，put on 也可用於其他物品的穿戴，例如：put on your hat/gloves/ring/headset/seat belt（戴上帽子／手套／戒指／耳機／安全帶）。

例
- Susan put on a robe after taking a shower.
  蘇珊淋浴後穿上一件長袍。

反 take off 脫掉

註1 put on 亦可作「塗抹」解，如：put on some sunscreen（擦些防曬乳）、put on some mosquito repellent（擦些防蚊液）、put on makeup（上妝）、put on foundation and blush（上粉底及腮紅）。

註2 put on weight 則指「體重增加」。

---

❿ be in/out 流行／過時

be（是；表狀態）＋ in（流行）＝ 流行
be（是；表狀態）＋ out（過時）＝ 過時

解說 要注意：此處的 in/out 皆為形容詞，意思分別為「流行／過時」。

例
- Miniskirts are in at the moment.
  現在流行迷你裙。

25

Lesson 2

- Long skirts are out right now.
  現在長裙已不流行。

同　　fashionable、in fashion 流行

反　　unfashionable、out of fashion 過時

活用狄克生片語　Lesson 2 複習測驗

一、選擇題（請選出一個最適當的選項）

1. I played basketball so much, my shoes were _____.
   (A) worn out　　(B) picked out　(C) put out　　(D) tired out

2. I _____ a nice gift for my mother at the store.
   (A) took off　　(B) put on　　(C) picked out　(D) got out

3. I wanted new furniture to bring my house _____.
   (A) upside down　(B) out-of-date　(C) up-to-date　(D) up-in-date

4. You put your shirt on backwards; it's _____.
   (A) picked out　(B) inside out　(C) upside down　(D) put out

二、翻譯填空

1. 去上好的餐館時，她喜歡盛裝打扮。
   She likes to _____ _____ when she goes to a nice restaurant.

2. 一季一季追隨時下流行是很辛苦的。
   It is difficult to follow what fashions _____ _____ from season to season.

3. 你瘦了不少，所以我們必須將你的褲子改小。
   You've lost a lot of weight so we need to _____ your pants _____.

三、中翻英

1. 你如果沒試，怎麼知道合不合身？

   _____

2. 當我從學校回家，我就脫下制服放輕鬆。

   _____

3. 第一次揹上我沈重的書包時，我差點跌倒。

   _____

解答請參閱第253頁

Notes

Lesson 3

居家生活 Family Life

Track 3

On weekends I usually stay in.¹ Sometimes a friend or two will stop by.² It can get lonely, but you get used to³ it after a while.

It's not my mother's fault. She brought me up⁴ to obey the rules and I broke them.

My parents don't ask me to do much around the house, but one time they called on⁵ me to clean out⁶ the hall closet and put away⁷ all my clothes.

Well, that morning I didn't get up⁸ until nearly eleven o'clock and I wanted to see off⁹ my best friend who was going to Europe for three weeks on vacation.

By the time I did my hair and made my face up,¹⁰ I didn't have time to clean out the closet or put my things away. I left the house without doing anything they had asked me to do.

I guess I have to agree with them. I should be grounded for a month.

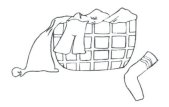

Lesson 3

❶ stay in/out　待在家／待外面

> **stay**（停留）＋ **in**（在家）　＝ 待在家
> **stay**（停留）＋ **out**（在外面）＝ 待外面

解說　in 和 out 在此皆為副詞，用來表明所在的位置是家裡或外面，其後不必加受詞。

例
- I plan to stay in this weekend and read some good books.
  我這週末打算待在家裡讀些好書。

- My mom won't let me stay out late.
  我媽不會讓我在外頭待太晚。

同　stay home 待在家

---

❷ stop by　稍事停留；順道拜訪

> **stop**（逗留）＋ **by**（經過）＝ 經過逗留

解說　stop by 是指經過某地「稍事停留」或「順道拜訪」某人，亦可說成 stop in/off/over。

例
- If you're in the neighborhood, please stop by and say hello.
  如果你到附近來，請順道過來打聲招呼。

似　drop by、come around/over「順道拜訪；過來坐坐」

居家生活 **Family Life**

❸ get used to　逐漸適應或習慣

get（達到……狀態）＋ **used to**（習慣於）＝ 適應；習慣於

解說　這裡的 get 可用 become 代替，get/become used to 是指對……「逐漸適應或習慣」。

例
- Stress is a fact of life, so you'd better get used to it.
  生活中難免會有壓力，你最好能習慣。

比　以下這幾個和 used 相關的用語，在意思上必須加以區別：

1. used to 以前經常；過去習慣
2. be used to 已習慣……
3. get/become used to 逐漸適應或習慣

---

❹ bring up　撫養長大　（可分開片語）

bring（帶來）＋ **up**（上升）＝ 拉拔長大

解說　bring up 比其相似詞 raise 還要來得傳神，因為大家都是從小由父母辛苦「拉拔長大」。

例
- Mike worked hard to bring up his three children.
  麥克辛苦工作養育三個孩子。

註　bring up 亦有「提出（問題、議題）」之意。

- Jim always brings up old issues when he argues with his girlfriend.
  吉姆和女友吵架時老愛翻舊帳。

❺ call on　請求；要求

call（呼叫）＋ **on**（針對）＝ 請求；要求

解說　常以「call on + 人 + for + 事物」、「call on + 人 + to do」句型表示「要求某人做某事」。

例
- He called on his friends for help.
  = He called on his friends to help.
  他要求朋友幫忙。

註　call on 亦可解作「call（訪問）+ on（針對）= 拜訪某人」，但 call 作「訪問」解是屬於英式用法，如今已較少單獨使用。若要表示「拜訪」其後通常必須加上介系詞 on 或 at，有以下兩種用法：「call on + 人」、「call at + 地方」。

- I'll call on my uncle tomorrow.
  我明天要去拜訪我舅舅。

- Let's call at his place.
  我們到他家去拜訪。

❻ clean out　清理乾淨　（可分開片語）

clean（清理）＋ **out**（完全）＝ 往外清理乾淨

解說　out 在此雖作「完全」解，但仍具有其方向性，因此 clean out 是指將容器、地方的髒污或垃圾「向外清理乾淨」。

居家生活 **Family Life**

例
- Julie hated cleaning out her father's ashtray.
  茱莉討厭清理她爸爸的煙灰缸。

比　以下這幾個和 clean 相關的用語，意思都是「清理乾淨」，但在用法上卻有些許不同：

1. **clean off/down** 是指將附在物體上的髒污「刷掉或洗掉」。
2. **clean out** 是指將容器、地方的髒污或垃圾「向外清理乾淨」。
3. **clean up** 是指將一個地方「整個清理乾淨」，此外，亦可指用餐前簡單的「梳洗」。

---

❼ put away　收拾好　（可分開片語）

put（放）＋ **away**（遠離）＝ 遠離現場擺放

解說　put away 並不像字面意思只是將東西「遠離現場擺放」，真正的意思是將東西「收拾好（放回原位）」。

例
- You have to put away all your toys before you can have dinner.
  你必須把你所有玩具都收拾好才能吃晚餐。

似　**put aside** 暫時擱置一旁

33

Lesson 3

❽ get up　起床　　　可分開片語

$$\boxed{\text{get}（達到……狀態）} + \boxed{\text{up}（起來）} = \boxed{站起來；起床}$$

解說　「起床」除可用 get up 表示，也可說成 get out of bed。相對地，go to bed 則是「上床睡覺」。

例
- I go to bed early and I get up early.
  我睡得早也起得早。

註　據說，如果早上起來從與平常相反的一側下床，便會造成一整天心情不好，因此「早上起來心情不好」便可用 get up on the wrong side of the bed = get out of bed on the wrong side 來表示。

---

❾ see off　送行　　　可分開片語

$$\boxed{\text{see}（看見）} + \boxed{\text{off}（離開）} = \boxed{目送離開}$$

解說　see off 分為自願與強迫兩種，第一種是指到機場、車站等地為親友「送行」，第二種則指強行被警衛等「送走；趕走」，常以「see + 人 + off」的形式出現。

例
- I saw my parents off at the airport.
  我到機場為父母送行。

聯　see out 送到門口

❿ make up   化妝   可分開片語

make（製作）＋ up（完成）＝ 製作完成

解說　make up 這個片語雖有多種含意，但意思大多是指「將不足、不完整的補足、做好、完成」，例如：

1. 化妝：讓臉上的缺陷不顯現
2. 和解：將彼此的誤解、閒隙補起來
3. 補考：讓沒過的科目有機會補考過
4. 補償：彌補別人的損失
5. 捏造：讓虛構的事情、故事得以呈現
6. 組成：指出整體是由哪些部分所構成 (此義為不可分片語)

例
- For the play, they made him up as an old man.
  在這齣戲裡，他們把他化妝成一位老頭子。

同　wear makeup、put on makeup「化妝」
makeup 在此為名詞，意思是「化妝品」，但請注意 wear makeup 是指「化好妝的狀態」，而 put on makeup 則指「化妝的動作」。

活用狄克生片語　　Lesson 3 複習測驗

一、選擇題（請選出一個最適當的選項）

1. It's raining outside, so let's _____ this afternoon.
   (A) staying inside　(B) stay in　　(C) stop by　　(D) call on

2. When my friends _____, I offer them something to drink.
   (A) stop by　　(B) get used to　(C) see me out　(D) stay in

3. It's hard to wake up early, but you'll _____ it after a while.
   (A) stay in　　(B) call on　　(C) get used to　(D) stop by

4. My parents often _____ me to clean up my room.
   (A) call on　　(B) get used to　(C) stay in　　(D) stop by

二、翻譯填空

1. 我清理衣櫥發現一封舊的信。
   I _____ _____ my closet and found an old letter.

2. 熟練的演員知道如何自行化妝。
   Skilled actors know how to _____ _____ their own _____.

3. 我必須六點起床趕搭公車上學。
   I have to _____ _____ at six o'clock to _____ the bus to school.

三、中翻英

1. 我祖母每當假期結束為我們送行時，總是很難過。
   _____

2. 家人吃完飯後，我們姊妹必須收拾所有餐盤。
   _____

3. 我父母撫養我長大，讓我成為一個好公民。
   _____

Lesson 4

開車 Driving

Billy Bean is an ice-cream truck driver. Kids go crazy when they hear the song from his truck, but Billy Bean hates kids. They only want his ice cream.

His only friends are his dog, Kazoo, and me. Kazoo licks berry-banana ice cream and sits next to Billy as he drives. I hate ice cream.

One day, Billy's dog got lost.[1] He ran away when Billy dropped off[2] some ice cream at the store.

The truck drove up to[3] my house. Billy told me what happened. He made room for[4] me in the truck and told me to get in.[5]

The ice-cream truck song started and kids came running. Billy got angry and backed up[6] fast because kids were trying to get on[7] the truck.

Kazoo was also trying to get on the truck. I tried to tell Billy to slow down,[8] but he ran right over[9] Kazoo.

This is why Billy Bean doesn't sell berry-banana ice cream, now. It's also why he doesn't play the ice-cream truck song anymore.

I ran into[10] him the other day. Now he drives the truck around the neighborhood slowly and silently.

Lesson 4

❶ get lost 迷路；滾開

get（達到某狀態）＋ **lost**（失去的）＝ 失去；遺失

解說 get lost 在此是指 lose one's direction「失去了方向」，也就是「迷路」。此外，get lost 亦可粗魯地用來叫人 go away「滾開」。

例
- He got lost in the side streets of Paris.
  他在巴黎的小巷道迷了路。

❷ drop off 中途下車　　可分開片語

drop（使下降）＋ **off**（離開）＝ 讓人（從交通工具）下來

解說 drop 或 drop off 皆可指載人到某地後，讓他自行下車。由於兩者皆須表明下車的地點，無法單獨使用，因此在用法和語意上幾乎沒有什麼差別。

例
- Bill asked the taxi driver to drop him off on the street corner.
  比爾要求計程車司機讓他在街角下車。

❸ drive up to 開往；駛近

drive（駕駛）＋ **up to**（朝……靠近）＝ 駛近

解說 up to 在這裡的意思比較特別，但也不是不常見，例如：go/run/walk up to（朝……前進／跑過去／走過去）。

例
- We drove up to Taipei to join Chris.
  我們開往台北與克里斯會合。

---

❹ make room for　　讓位；騰出空間

make（做出）+ **room**（空間）+ **for**（為了）=　為……騰出空間

解說　room 在此為不可數名詞，指「空間；場所」。用於人，指「讓位」；用於物，則指「挪出空間以容納或擺放」。

例
- Susan made room for an old lady on the bus.
  蘇珊讓位給公車上一位老太太。

聯　move over 挪開、挪過去（以騰出空間）

---

❺ get in　　上車（小型車）

get（達到）+ **in**（在裡面）= 進到裡面

解說　搭乘小型汽車時，由於一上車就直接進到車裡去了，不像大型交通工具要沿著踏板或階梯等上車或登機，所以要用 get in 不可用 get on。

例
- We got in the car and headed for the post office.
  我們上了車，開往郵局。

反　get out of 下車（僅用於小型車，大型交通工具要用 get off）

❻ back up　倒車；向後退　[可分開片語]

back（後退）＋ **up**（完全）＝ 向後退

解說　動詞 back 本身就有「倒車」的意思，如果單獨使用，其後必須指出倒車的位置，如：Could you back your car onto the driveway?（麻煩你將車子倒到車道上。）；若用 back up 來表示「倒車」，由於 up 為副詞，因此後面並不一定要表明倒車的位置，如：Please back up.（請倒車。）。

例
- Could you back the truck up a little more?
  麻煩你將卡車後退一點好嗎？

註1　back up 亦可表示「車流回堵」，如：
- The accident had backed up traffic for miles.
  這起車禍讓車流回堵了好幾英里。

註2　back up 也常作「支持」解，這時的 back 是指「在背後給予支撐」。

---

❼ get on　上車（大型交通工具）

get（達到）＋ **on**（在……上）＝ 登上

解說　搭乘巴士、火車、飛機等大型交通工具時，由於有沿著踏板或階梯等上車或登機的動作，因此常會用 get on 或 go/get aboard 來表示；而小型汽車由於一上車就直接進到車裡去了，所以要用 get in 不可用 get on。

開車 Driving

例
- You get on the Red Line for two stops and change to the Yellow Line.
  你搭紅線到第二站下車轉搭黃線。

反　get off 下車（用於大型交通工具，小型車要用 get out of）

---

❽ slow down　放慢速度

slow（放慢速度）＋ **down**（降低）＝ 放慢速度

解說　slow 和 slow down 皆可指「放慢速度」，常可交替使用，唯一的差別是 slow 後面要接受詞或說明，不可單獨使用，而 slow down 卻可單獨使用。

例
- Could you slow down a little? I'm not in a rush.
  請你開慢一點，我不趕時間。

同　slow up 放慢速度（使用頻率較 slow down 低）

反　speed up 加快速度

---

❾ run over　輾過

可分開片語

run（跑；移動）＋ **over**（越過）＝ 輾過

解說　常以被動語態 be/get run over 表示人、物等被車輛「輾過」。

Lesson 4

例
- Bob nearly ran over a cat on his drive to work.
  巴伯在開車上班途中差點壓到一隻貓。

- She was almost run over by a scooter while walking across the street yesterday.
  她昨天過馬路的時候，差點被一輛機車輾過去。

註　run over 亦有「匆忙看過」、「重複練習」、「重新講解、說明」等意思。

---

❿ run into　不期而遇；撞上

run（跑；移動）＋ **into**（進入）＝ 跑入；闖入；撞上；遇見

解說　run into 若作「撞上」解，多半是指交通工具的碰撞，力道較為猛烈；若指人與人、人與物之間的碰撞，則常會用 bump into 來表示。

由於這兩個片語都有「不期而遇」和「撞上」這兩個意思，因此片語後面如果接人時，必須根據上下文分辨其意。

例
- The car ran into a tree.
  這車子撞上了一棵樹。

- I ran into my old boyfriend while shopping yesterday.
  我昨天購物時，恰巧遇到了我的前男友。

似　bump into、run across、come across 皆可指「不期而遇」

活用狄克生片語　Lesson 4 複習測驗

一、選擇題（請選出一個最適當的選項）

1. If you _____, call me and I'll tell you how to get here.
   (A) get lost　　(B) get out　　(C) drop off　　(D) slow down

2. The mailman _____ my house and gave me a letter.
   (A) broke into　(B) dropped off　(C) drove up to　(D) slow down

3. I don't ride the bus to school; my mother _____ me _____.
   (A) drives . . . up　(B) takes . . . off　(C) backs . . . up　(D) drops . . . off

4. The car was really full, but they _____ me and I got in.
   (A) drive up to　(B) got lost　　(C) made room for　(D) backed up

二、翻譯填空

1. 車子開過來，打開車門，我上了車和他們一起走。
   The car came and opened the door; I _____ _____ and went with them.

2. 我們再也無法向前開，所以我們就倒車離開。
   We couldn't drive forward anymore, so we _____ _____ and left.

3. 公車上有太多人，所以我上不了車。
   There were too many people on the bus, so I couldn't _____ _____.

三、中翻英

1. 如果我朋友車開太快又不願放慢速度，我就再也不和他們一起坐車。

2. 昨天我在路上輾過一隻小鳥。

3. 在路上遇到我的小學老師總是令我高興。

Notes

Lesson 5

旅遊 Trips

Sometimes my father takes us with him on business trips. He doesn't look forward to[1] it, but we do. It's a time for my brother and me to goof off.[2]

We get excited when we set out[3] on the trip.

While he is packing his suits and documents, we pack our bathing suits. It's the only thing we need.

At the airport, my brother and I line up[4] and begin arguing about who will sit next to the window. After we check in[5] at the hotel, we go to the pool. Swimming in a hotel pool is the best. While my father is working hard, we're taking it easy[6] and working out.[7]

I know my dad feels a little sad because he can't take time off[8] and take part in[9] the fun, but he's happy to see us having a good time.[10]

❶ look forward to　期待；盼望

look（看）＋ **forward**（向前）＋ **to**（向；往）＝ 引首期盼

解說　look forward to 是指「期待；盼望」某事，其中的 to 為介系詞而非不定詞，常以「look forward to + V-ing / N.」句型出現。

例
- I am looking forward to playing basketball with Tony.
  我期待和湯尼一起打籃球。

似　expect 預期；期待

註　not look forward to 並不是指「不期待」，而是指「不期望發生的事卻發生了」。

---

❷ goof off　混日子；打混

goof（懶散）＋ **off**（離開）＝ 懶散不做事

解說　goof 當名詞時意為「傻瓜；笨蛋」，作動詞是指「懶散；搞砸」。goof off 這個片語源自美國軍中，原指阿兵哥偷懶、打混。如今，常指職場上「打混；摸魚」或在日常生活中「無所事事」、「懶散度日」。

例
- Tony's been goofing off at school lately.
  湯尼最近老是在學校打混。

似　goof around「閒蕩；混日子」、fool around「鬼混；胡鬧」

旅遊 Trips

❸ set out　出發；開始

set（朝某方向）＋ **out**（向外）＝ 出發

解說　set out 作「出發」解時，除單獨使用外，還有以下兩個常見的句型：
1.「set out on + 旅程」
2.「set out for + 地方」

例
- Before we set out on our journey, we should check that we have prepared everything we need.
  在起程上路之前，我們應該檢查看看一切所需是否準備齊全。

- We set out for the farm in the morning, hoping to make it there by noon.
  我們早上起程去農莊，希望能在中午前抵達。

似　set off（出發；啟程）、head/leave for（前往、出發到某地）

註　set out 也有「開始；著手」之意，以下是兩種常見的句型：
1.「set out to do」
2.「set out on + 事物」

❹ line up　排隊

line（排成一線）＋ **up**（上升；增加）＝ 排成一列

解說　line up 是指 stand in line「排隊；排成一線」，英式的說法為 queue up。

47

Lesson 5

例
- Would you mind lining up?
  請排隊好嗎？

聯 cut in line 插隊

似 line up 可引申指「排隊搶著要；爭相要」，例如：

- Young people are lining up to appear on reality TV shows.
  年輕人都爭相要上真人實境電視節目。

❺ check in/out　住／退房登記

check（核對）＋ **in**（向內）＝ 辦理報到、住房登記
check（核對）＋ **out**（向外）＝ 辦理借出、退房登記

解說 check in 除指「住房登記」外，亦可指到機場「登記報到」或「託運」行李等；check out 一般是指在旅館、超市的櫃檯「結帳離開」或在圖書館「登記借閱」，此外，亦有「檢查」、「確認」之意。

例
- I'd like to check in for flight DT123.
  我想辦理 DT123 班機的登機手續。

- We will go to the airport after we check out of our hotel.
  我們退房後就會前往機場。

❻ take it easy　放輕鬆

take（承擔）＋ **it**（事物）＋ **easy**（輕鬆地）＝ 輕鬆看待事物

| 旅遊 Trips

解說 it 是指「事物」，因此 take it easy 亦可說成 take things easy，常用來表示「放鬆心情」或要別人「別緊張」。

例
- I'm just going to take it easy on the weekend; I don't have any plans.
  我週末只想放輕鬆，沒有任何計畫。

註 take it easy 也可表示「不嚴格對待；手下留情」，例如：

- The coach took it easy on the new players.
  教練對新球員並不苛求。

---

❼ work out　健身；擬定（計畫等）

work（努力）＋ out（顯現出來）＝ 努力而有進展或結果

解說 work out 常指到健身房作「運動；健身」，其名詞為 workout。

例
- Frank works out at the gym three times a week.
  法蘭克每週去健身房健身三次。

比 有道是 Exercise is the best way to get fit.（運動是健身的最好方法。）exercise（運動）泛指所有的戶內、戶外運動，而 work out 通常是指去健身房作運動，而非戶外運動。

註 但 work out 還有許多其他意思，如：「解決」問題、「想出」答案、「擬定；提出」計畫等。(以上皆為可分開動詞)

❽ take (time) off　休假；休息

take（取得）＋ **time**（時間）＋ **off**（離開）＝ 取得時間離開

解說　在使用時，其中的 time 通常會用實際休假的時間長短來表示，例如：take two days off（請兩天假）、take the afternoon off（下午請假）。

例
- I want to take three days off next week.
  我下星期想請三天假。

似　have (time) off 休假；休息

聯　give (someone) time off（准假）、on the go（忙個不停）。

---

❾ take part (in)　參加

take（取得）＋ **part**（關聯）＋ **in**（在……之中）＝ 取得關聯參與其中

解說　常以「take part in ＋ 事物」句型出現，但如果後面不加事物，take part 亦可單獨使用。

例
- Dan pulled a muscle and was unable to take part in the track meet.
  丹拉傷了肌肉，無法參加田徑賽。

- Susan really wanted to take part but she was too busy.
  蘇珊實在太忙，不然她很想參加。

旅遊 Trips

❿ have a good time　玩得愉快

have（擁有）+ **a good time**（一段美好時光）= 擁有一段美好時光

[解說] have a good time 或 have fun 常用來祝福別人「玩得愉快」。

[例]
- I hope you'll have a good time at the party.
  我希望你們在派對上玩得愉快。

[聯] have a bad time 過得不好

活用狄克生片語　Lesson 5 複習測驗

一、選擇題（請選出一個最適當的選項）

1. I always _____ my summer vacation in America.
   (A) look forward to　(B) goof off　(C) set out　(D) check in

2. You shouldn't _____ in class; you should pay attention.
   (A) check in　(B) set out　(C) work out　(D) goof off

3. We'll _____ on the trip tomorrow at six in the morning.
   (A) take it easy　(B) goof off　(C) set off　(D) take part

4. If you want to get in to see the movie, you need to _____.
   (A) look out　(B) check up　(C) line up　(D) work out

二、翻譯填空

1. 入住旅館你必須先辦好住房登記。
   You'll need to _____ _____ at the hotel before you sleep there.

2. 除夕是參加家庭慶祝活動的時刻
   New Year's Eve is a time to _____ _____ _____ family celebrations.

3. 依我看，玩得開心並不比有責任感重要。
   In my view, _____ _____ _____ _____ is not as important as behaving responsibly.

三、中翻英

1. 我經常請假不上班讀有趣的書。

   _____

2. 休假是放輕鬆享受人生的時候。

   _____

3. 我身體健康，因為我花時間每週健身三次。

   _____

Lesson 6

學習 Learning

Track 6

I went to school for a very long time. My friends joked that I was majoring in[1] "school".

Every night I would stay up[2] late to read over[3] the next day's assignments. I learned the lessons by heart[4] and I would hand in[5] my homework assignments on time.

University's a lot different than high school, so there's a lot to figure out.[6] You have to learn the ropes[7] pretty quickly. When the teacher calls the roll,[8] you better be in your seat, ready to work.

You can't be late all the time. If you don't believe me, look up[9] the word *expel* in your dictionary. And this time don't use your electronic dictionary. Use a real book.

You wouldn't want to lose your touch[10] with books. For the next four years, they're going to be your best friends.

翻譯請參閱第256頁

❶ major in   主修

major（主修）＋ **in**（在……方面）＝ 主修

解說　「major in + 科目」屬於美式用法，之所以這樣用是因為美國人常將大學的 main subject（主修科目）稱之為 major。

例
- I'm majoring in math.
  我現在主修數學。

聯　minor in 輔修

---

❷ stay up   熬夜

stay（持續某狀態）＋ **up**（起來）＝ 維持起床的狀態

解說　字面意思是指（該睡的時候卻）不去睡，也就是「熬夜」。

例
- I stayed up late cramming.
  我熬夜 K 書到很晚。

似　burn the midnight oil（熬夜到很晚）、pull an all-nighter（整晚熬夜）

聯　night owl 夜貓子

學習 Learning

❸ read over　從頭到尾讀一遍

可分開片語

read（讀）**+ over**（從頭到尾）**=** 從頭到尾讀一遍

解說　常用來表示對書籍、文件等「從頭到尾」查看內容或找出錯誤作更正。

例
- I haven't had a chance to read it over carefully.
  我還沒有機會好好把它讀一遍。

同　read through 從頭到尾看一遍

---

❹ by heart　記住

by（用；靠）**+ heart**（心臟）**=** 用心臟

解說　常以 know/learn by heart 句型表示「記住；背誦」，我們當然知道記東西是靠腦子而不是靠 heart（心臟），但既然這已形成固定的片語，我們也只好給它「記住」。

例　Actors usually have to learn their lines by heart.
演員通常必須記臺詞。

同　memorize 記住；背誦

比　keep in mind 常用來提醒人「要記得某事」、「要將某事放在心上」，意思與 by heart 略有不同。

❺ hand in　繳交

hand（用手拿給）＋ in（向裡面）＝ 交到……的手上

解說　一般是指將文件、資料、作業等交給老師或主管。

例
- I'd like you to hand in your homework assignment on time.
  請你準時交家庭作業。

比　turn in 是指將事物「交還；交給」原所有人、失物招領處或警察局，例如：

- When the lease ended, Julie turned in the keys to the landlord.
  租約到期，茱莉就把鑰匙還給房東。

❻ figure out　想出；弄清楚

figure（計算；想像）＋ out（顯現出來）＝ 算出；想出

解說　figure 作名詞用時有「數字；圖形」之意，作動詞時可指「計算；想像」，因此 figure out 便有「想出（辦法）」、「弄清楚；搞懂」等含意。

例
- I still haven't figured out how to solve that problem.
  我還沒想出如何解那個問題。

學習 Learning

❼ learn the ropes　學會訣竅

learn（學會）＋ **the ropes**（繩索）＝ 學會繩索結構

[解說] 原指水手需花許多時間、精力，才能「熟悉船上的許多索具及船帆等複雜結構」。後來，常引申指「熟悉工作的內容；懂得訣竅」。

[例]
- Jill is new in the office, so she hasn't learned the ropes yet.
  吉兒是公司的新人，所以她還抓不到訣竅。

[似] know the ropes 懂得訣竅

[聯] show someone the ropes 教某人做事的訣竅

❽ call the roll　點名

call（大聲念）＋ **the roll**（點名簿）＝ 點名

[解說] call/take the roll 主要用於學校老師點名，其名詞形式為 roll call。

[例]
- The teacher came in and started to call the roll.
  老師進來開始點名。

- If you're late, you'll miss the roll call.
  你如果遲到，就會錯過點名。

Lesson 6

❾ look up　查閱；查詢　　可分開片語

look（看）＋ **up**（作強調）＝ 努力查看

解説　up 若作「向上」解，look up 的意思便是「抬頭看」、「有起色；好轉」；在此 up 則是「作強調」用，因此 look up 的意思就變成：「查閱；查詢」字典、電話簿或資料等。

例
- She looked up at Jimmy with sad eyes.
  她失望地抬頭看著吉米。
- If you don't recognize a word, you should look it up in the dictionary.
  如果不認得某字，就該查字典。

似　consult 查詢；諮詢

---

❿ lose one's touch　變生疏

lose（失去）＋ **one's**（某人的）＋ **touch**（觸感）＝ 某人失去觸感

解説　原指音樂家失去彈奏樂器的觸感，如今，常引申指對事物、工作等「變得生疏」。

例
- Has Warren Buffett lost his touch?
  華倫‧巴菲特是否寶刀已老？

比　lose touch with (someone) 和某人失去聯絡

活用狄克生片語　Lesson 6 複習測驗

一、選擇題（請選出一個最適當的選項）

1. I _____ history at school; now I'm a history teacher.
   (A) majored in　　(B) stay up for　　(C) read over　　(D) looked up

2. I can't _____ late because I need to wake up early.
   (A) work up　　(B) stay up　　(C) set out　　(D) hold out

3. Before your test, you need to _____ your notes several times.
   (A) major in　　(B) stay up　　(C) pick out　　(D) read over

4. I don't need to read the words; I know my country's song _____.
   (A) by turns　　(B) by remember　　(C) by heart　　(D) in the long run

二、翻譯填空

1. 我記得當老師點名叫到我的名字時，我有多麼緊張。
   I remember how nervous I felt when the teacher _____ _____ _____ and said my name.

2. 我認為學習外語最好的方法就是花時間查你不認識的字。
   I think the best way to learn a _____ language is to take the time to _____ _____ the words you don't know.

3. 我學到一件事就是，如果你不持續練習，你就會變生疏。
   One thing I've learned is that if you don't keep practicing, you'll _____ _____ _____.

三、中翻英

1. 老師要求我們繳交上週的家庭作業。
   _____

2. 我是班上第一個想出這個數學問題。
   _____

3. 在這裡工作一陣子後，你就會學到訣竅。
   _____

Notes

Lesson 7

健康 Health

As the seasons change we often start to get tired[1] easily. If you begin to feel a little under the weather,[2] start looking after[3] yourself.

Start taking extra vitamin C to help build up[4] your resistance. Even if you do catch cold,[5] you'll be able to get over[6] it faster.

Some people believe that if you put on weight,[7] you won't get sick[8] as easily. However, doctors say there is no truth to this. If you get plenty of rest and drink lots of fluids but still don't feel better in a few days, send for[9] the doctor. Don't leave the house in a weakened state or you may pass out.[10]

Lesson 7

❶ get tired　疲倦

get（變得）＋ **tired**（疲倦的）＝ 疲倦

解說　其他常見的用法有：be tired（疲倦）、look tired（看起來有倦容）、feel tired（覺得累）。

例
- When I was young, I never used to get tired so easily.
  我年輕時，從不會這麼容易累。

聯　tired out、worn out、exhausted 皆表示「筋疲力盡；非常疲累」

比　be/get tired of 對……感到厭煩

---

❷ under the weather　身體不適

under（受影響）＋ **the weather**（天氣）＝ 受天氣影響

解說　源自天氣對人身體健康的影響，引申指「身體不適」，而通常都不是很嚴重的疾病。

例
- Please excuse my coughing. I've been under the weather these last few days.
  抱歉我在咳嗽，我這幾天身體不舒服。

健康 Health

❸ look after　照顧;照料

look（看）**+ after**（追蹤）**=** 追蹤地看

[解說] look after 是指「照顧;照料」而不是「看後面」,這是一個不可分片語,所有受詞都必須接在介系詞 after 後面。

[例]
- Who will look after your pets when you go on vacation?
  你去度假時誰會照顧你的寵物?

[同] take care of 照顧;照料

[聯] be able to look after yourself 有辦法照顧自己

---

❹ build up　增進;增強　　可分開片語

build（建立）**+ up**（上升;增加）**=** 建立發展;增進

[解說] build up 除指「逐漸建立發展」外,亦有「增進;增強」之意。

[例]
- I want to build up my English-speaking skills.
  我想要加強我的英文口語能力。

[註] build up 還可用來表示「吹捧;吹噓」,例如:

- My sister built me up as a great tennis player to her friends.
  我姊姊跟她朋友吹噓說我是個網球高手。

63

❺ catch cold　感冒

catch（染上）＋ **cold**（感冒）＝ 染上感冒

解說　catch 主要用於傳染性的疾病，如：catch the flu（得了流行性感冒）、catch chicken pox（得了水痘），而句型「catch ＋ 疾病 ＋ from ＋ 人」則指「被某人傳染某疾病」。

例
- She caught cold from her elder sister.
  她被姊姊傳染了感冒。

註　cold 可當可數名詞，因此「感冒」也可說成 catch a cold，而 a bad/heavy cold 即指「重感冒」。

❻ get over　復原

get（達到）＋ **over**（越過）＝ 越過；克服

解說　句型「get over ＋ 疾病」的字面意思是「克服了某疾病」，即「復原」之意。

例
- It's taken me ages to get over my cold.
  我感冒了好久才好。

似　recover from 恢復；復原

註　get over it 與疾病無關，常用來告訴別人「將……忘懷；從……中恢復過來」別再傷心、難過。

健康　Health

❼ put on weight　增加體重

put on（增加）＋**weight**（體重）＝增加體重

解說　其中的 weight 可用實際的重量作代替，如：put on three pounds/kilos（胖了三磅／公斤）。

例
- Chris put on so much weight that his jeans didn't fit.
  克里斯胖了很多，所以他的牛仔褲穿不下。

同　gain weight 增加體重

反　lose weight 減肥

聯　watch (one's) weight（注意自己的體重）、have a weight problem（有體重上的問題）

---

❽ get sick　生病

get（得到；變得）＋**sick**（生病的）＝生病

解說　也常用 be sick 來表示「生病」，但 be sick 在英式用法裡卻是指「噁心；反胃」，所以如果要明確表示「想吐」可用 be sick to one's stomach。此外，也可將疾病名稱直接加到 get 後面，如：get cold（感冒）、get food poisoning（食物中毒）。

例
- I didn't wonder at his not coming to school; he got sick often.
  他常生病，所以我對他不能來學校一點也不訝異。

Lesson 7

| 比 | come down with 得了……病 |

| 似 | feel sick 作嘔；想吐 |

| 聯 | call in sick（打電話請病假）、be out sick（因生病而沒來） |

---

❾ send for　延請某人

send（使前往）＋ for（針對）＝ 使針對……前往

| 解說 | 「send for + 人」是指「延請某人過來」；「send for + 事物」則指「派人為你去處理或拿」某事物。 |

| 例 | • I think we have to send for a doctor.
我想我們必須請位醫生來。 |

---

❿ pass out　昏倒；分發

pass（轉移）＋ out（向外）＝ 轉移向外

| 解說 | pass out 是個口語用法，比喻一個人的知覺被轉移出去，也就是「失去知覺」、「昏倒」之意。 |

| 例 | • When I saw all the blood, I almost passed out.
我看到這麼多血差點昏倒。 |

| 同 | faint、pass out cold 昏倒 |

| 註 | pass out 亦可指將東西「分發；分配」出去，意思相當於 give out、hand out。（此時為可分開片語） |

活用狄克生片語　Lesson 7 複習測驗

一、選擇題（請選出一個最適當的選項）

1. If you don't eat well, you can _____ easily.
   (A) run down　　(B) get over　　(C) build up　　(D) get tired

2. I didn't go to work because I felt _____.
   (A) built up　　(B) passed out　　(C) got over　　(D) under the weather

3. When you grow up, you should learn how to _____ yourself.
   (A) check up　　(B) dress up　　(C) work out　　(D) look after

4. I lift weights, because I want to _____ my muscles.
   (A) build up　　(B) run over　　(C) run past　　(D) pass out

二、翻譯填空

1. 我因為忘記帶傘淋濕而感冒。
   I _____ _____ because I forgot to bring my umbrella and got wet.

2. 上週我生病了，但我復原後現在覺得很好。
   I was sick last week, but I _____ _____ it and feel fine now.

3. 我通常在節慶期間體重會增加，因為我吃太多了。
   I usually _____ _____ _____ during the holiday season because I eat so much.

三、中翻英

1. 我小時候經常生病，但我已學會照顧自己的身體。

   _____

2. 我想我們該請位醫生來。

   _____

3. 有一天我籃球打得太劇烈而差點昏倒。

   _____

Notes

Lesson 8

解釋說明 Explanation

According to[1] *On Vacation, a Handbook for Families on Holiday*, families vacationing together account for[2] 46 percent of all vacationers in the US.

As for[3] the other 54 percent, holiday researchers point out[4] that it includes nearly everyone else. "Holidays are good for family communication," says Hubert Shingleskin. "For example,[5] many parents find they can get through to[6] their teens in the woods easier than in the living room."

In terms of[7] quality time with your children, in the woods you will have nothing but[8] time.

On the other hand,[9] there is the real possibility that your children will be bitter. Teenagers don't want to be dragged away from the mall, let alone[10] the comforts of home.

Lesson 8

❶ according to　根據；遵照

according（根據）＋ **to**（針對）＝ 根據；遵照

解說　according to 整個片語作介系詞用，其後常接所根據的資訊、消息或規則等

例
- According to many legends, vampires come out at night.
  根據許多傳說，吸血鬼常在夜間出沒。

聯　go according to plan 依計行事

註　但若是「根據某人的意見、看法」則不可用 according to 要用
in (one's) opinion/view 或 (one's) opinion is that 等來表示。

---

❷ account for　佔了……；說明

account（計算；說明）＋ **for**（針對）＝ 佔……部分；針對……解釋說明

解說　account for 一般是指針對事情的原因「作解釋說明」，亦可指某事物在數量或比例上「佔了……」。

例
- Taiwan accounts for 30 percent of all sales in Asia.
  台灣佔整個亞洲區銷售額的百分之三十。
- Can you account for your absence this Monday?
  你可以解釋一下這星期一為什麼沒來？

似　explain 說明；解釋

解釋說明 Explanation

❸ as for 至於；關於

as（如……）+ **for**（針對）=　至於……

解說　as for 是指就剛才所說或所談的，引導出另一個相關或受影響的人、事或物。

例
- You can ask Susan, but as for me, I'd rather stay at home.
  你可以問一下蘇珊，至於我，我寧願待在家裡。

似　as to 關於（相當於concerning，並無引導作用）

可分開片語

❹ point out 指出

point（指向）+ **out**（顯現出來）=　指出；指給……看

解說　有以下幾種常見的句型：「point out + that 子句」、「point out + 事物」、「point out + 事物 + to 人」，由於 point out 為可分開片語，因此受詞若為代名詞必須放在片語中間，若為一般名詞則放中間或後面皆可。

例
- Thank you for pointing out this mistake to me.
  謝謝你向我指出這個錯誤。

似　indicate（指示；指出）、show（呈現；顯示）

Lesson 8

❺ for example 例如

for（以……的目的）**+ example**（例子）**=** 比方說

解說 這是舉例說明時常用的片語，可縮寫成 e.g. 或 eg。

例
- For example, to cut costs, we could make the monthly birthday party BYOB.
  比方說，為了降低成本，我們可以要大家在每個月慶生會時自備飲料。
  （註: BYOB = bring your own beer/booze/bottle）

同 for instance

聯 follow someone's example（學某人的榜樣）、set an example（樹立榜樣）、make an example of someone（殺雞儆猴）

---

❻ get through to 使瞭解；聯絡上

get（達到）**+ through**（順利通過）**+ to**（到）
= 順利送達、聯絡上、使人瞭解

解說 get through to 除表示將事物「送達；傳達」外，常用來表示用通訊工具「聯絡上」某人，亦有「使人瞭解（某事）」之意。

例
- Paula couldn't get through to Mr. Brown until after lunch.
  寶拉一直到午餐後才打通布朗先生的電話。

- I don't seem to be able to get through to him.
  我似乎無法讓他瞭解。

❼ in terms of 就……而言

in（以）+ **terms**（措辭）+ **of**（的）＝ 以……的措辭、說法

解說 複數 terms 常用來表示「條件」、「關係；情誼」或「措辭；說法」，在此是指「措辭；說法」，而 in terms of 有兩種意思，一是「以……的字眼、口吻」，也可作「以……角度、觀點」解。

例
- The department store is superior to the night market in terms of choice and quality.
  就選擇性和品質來說，百貨公司比夜市好多了。

聯 in the long/middle/short term 長期／中期／短期而言

---

❽ nothing but 只是；只不過

nothing（無）+ **but**（除了）＝ 除了……之外什麼也沒有

解說 nothing but 可從字面「除了……之外什麼也沒有」作解讀，意思相當於 only「只是；根本就是；只不過」。

例
- You are nothing but a couch potato.
  你整天只會看電視。

- There was nothing but salad to eat.
  只有沙拉可吃。

❾ on the other hand　另一方面

on（在……上）＋ **the other**（另一個）＋ **hand**（方面）＝ 另一方面

解說　此處 hand 為抽象用法，意思是「方面」。on the other hand「另一方面」常跟在 on the one hand「一方面」後面與之連用，以引導出與前述相反的事實或觀點，常譯為「另一方面；相對而言；從另一角度來看」。

例
- Dogs are loyal to their owners. Cats, on the other hand, are more independent.
  狗對飼主忠心耿耿，相對而言，貓就比較獨立。

註　如前面已出現 on the one hand，後面的 on the other hand 可省略 hand，成為 on the other。

❿ let alone　更不用說

let（讓）＋ **alone**（單獨地）＝ 讓……單獨地

解說　若用於人，是指 let someone alone「讓某人獨處、靜一靜」；若用於事物，則指「更不必說」，也就是後面所提的事情根本不可能發生、連提都不用提，應讓它單獨存在。

例
- I don't have enough money to pay my rent, let alone buy a new car.
  我連房租都不夠錢付，更不用說買輛新車了。

似	not to mention、to say nothing of「更不用說」
註1	**let alone** 作連接詞用，經常用於否定句，前面常會加逗點將句子分成兩半，因此須注意句子兩端所接的詞性、時態必須一致。
註2	若指「讓某人獨處、靜一靜」使用 leave someone alone 的機率比較高。

活用狄克生片語　Lesson 8 複習測驗

一、選擇題（請選出一個最適當的選項）

1. 1. _____ many scientists, smoking is the worst thing for your body.
   (A) According to　(B) Account for　(C) As for　(D) In terms of

2. Car and motorcycle accidents _____ many young people's injuries.
   (A) make up for　(B) make out　(C) as for　(D) account for

3. My brother really dislikes basketball; _____ me, I love it.
   (A) as for　(B) account for　(C) according to　(D) for example

4. I like all kinds of deserts; _____, I love cake.
   (A) however　(B) by all means　(C) for example　(D) in terms of

二、翻譯填空

1. 我的老師指出我最近所寫文章上的許多問題。
   My teacher _____ _____ many problems with my most recent essay.

2. 有時候如果你用開玩笑的方式，比較容易讓人瞭解某個想法。
   It is sometimes easier to _____ an idea _____ _____ people if you make a joke.

3. 我在海外求學時，不太喜歡跟同學講話，更不用說是老師。
   When I studied abroad, I didn't feel comfortable talking to my classmates, _____ _____ the teachers.

三、中翻英

1. 我總想遵照父母的建議，但另一方面卻又想追尋自己的夢想。
   _____

2. 我只要你告訴我真相。
   _____

3. 就名與利而言，當醫生可能是最佳選擇。
   _____

Lesson 9

建議 Advice

> Track 9

I have dreams for my son like any father does. Whether those dreams come true[1] or fall through[2] is up to him.

My father taught me a work ethic and moral attitude that I believe holds good,[3] even today.

Sure it's a different world now. However, if all the negative things don't get the better of[4] you and you don't screw up[5] too badly, the dreams your parents have for you won't be in vain.[6]

Your future is at stake.[7] Like I told my son, carry out[8] your own dreams and don't give up.[9] My dream for you is that you succeed on your terms and never give in.[10]

Be as good as I know you are and better than you think you can be.

Lesson 9

❶ come true　成真;實現

come（成為）＋ **true**（真的）＝ 成真;實現

解說　用來表示希望、夢想、預言等「實現;成真」。

例
- If you work hard, your wish to study abroad will come true.
  你如果努力一點,出國留學的夢想就能成真。

註1　雖然 come 在這裡的意思是 become,但卻不可說成 become true。

註2　a dream come true 是個常見的說法,表示「夢想已成真」,完整的說法是 a dream that has come true,但其中的 that has 常會被省略不說。

似　carry out 執行;實現

---

❷ fall through　失敗;落空

fall（落下）＋ **through**（穿過）＝ 落空

解說　原指要接住或網住的東西,但卻給漏接或漏掉了,引申指「失敗;落空」。

例
- This plan fell through at the last minute.
  這項計劃功敗垂成。

似　fail 失敗

建議 Advice

❸ hold good　仍有效；仍適用

hold（維持）＋ **good**（有效的；適用的）＝ 仍然有效或適用的

解説　要注意 good 在這裡的意思是「有效的；適用的」，如：The ticket is good for all ages.（此票任何年齡皆適用。）；而 hold good 則指合約、規則、事物等「仍然有效或適用」。

例
- These study skills still hold good today.
  這些學習技巧到現在仍然適用。

同　hold true 仍有效；仍適用

---

❹ get the better of　打敗；勝過

get（得到）＋ **the better of**（比……好）＝ 佔了上風；勝過

解説　常以「人／事物 + get/have the better of + 人」的句型出現，以表示「被某人所擊敗、佔了上風」或「受挫於某事物；受某事物所驅使、控制」。

例
- My curiosity finally got the better of me and I opened the box.
  最後我忍不住好奇打開了這盒子。

同　get/have the best of 打敗；勝過

❺ screw up　搞砸

screw（用螺絲拴緊）＋ **up**（完全地）＝ 用螺絲拴緊

解說　這是一個俚俗用法，原指「用螺絲拴緊」，但在此 screw up 則是粗話 fuck up「搞砸；損毀」的委婉代用語。

例
- Ben screwed up the soup by adding too much water.
  班加了太多水，把那鍋湯搞砸了。

❻ in vain　徒勞無功

in（在……之中）＋ **vain**（枉然的）＝ 徒勞無功

解說　vain 表示「無效的；徒然的」，in vain 指「徒勞無功」，常作副詞用。

例
- I tried to learn German, but all my efforts were in vain.
  我努力學德文，可是怎麼學都學不會。

❼ at stake　瀕臨危險

at（以）＋ **stake**（賭注）＝ 以……為賭注

解說　stake 是「賭注；賭金」，而 at stake 除表「以……為賭注」外，常引申指「……瀕臨危險或處於緊要關頭」。

建議 Advice

> 例
> The athlete broke his arm, and now his career is at stake.
> 該名運動員跌斷了手臂,他的運動生涯正面臨危機。

---

❽ carry out　執行;實現

carry(搬運) + **out**(出來) = 搬出來;執行;實踐

> 解說
> carry out 原指將東西「搬運出來」,常引申指計畫、任務等的「實行;執行」或希望、夢想等的「實現;完成」。

> 例
> - We need to carry out further tests before we come up with a conclusion.
>   在提出結論之前,我們必須作進一步的測試。
>
> - The team carried out the coach's play perfectly.
>   該球隊完美地完成教練的指示。

> 似
> come true 成真;實現

---

❾ give up　放棄;戒除　（可分開片語）

give(讓與) + **up**(完全地) = 完全讓與

> 解說
> give up 除指「放棄」外,亦可指「戒除(習慣)」或「認輸;投降」。

Lesson 9

例
- Don't give up. We can still make a comeback.
  別放棄，我們還可以東山再起。

- Fred's New Year resolution was to give up eating chocolate.
  佛瑞德在新年下定決心戒掉吃巧克力的習慣。

聯　give up halfway（半途而廢）、give up on（對⋯⋯表示絕望）

似　abandon 拋棄；放棄

---

❿ give in　屈服；讓步

give（讓與）＋ in（向裡面）＝ 讓步向內

解說　若要表示「向⋯⋯屈服、讓步」則以「give in to ＋ 人／事物」來表示。

例
- Susan kept begging me for a new bicycle, until I finally gave in.
  蘇珊一直求我買輛新腳踏車給她，最後我還是拗不過她。

- If we gave in to them this time, they would ask for more next time.
  如果我們這次向他們讓步，下次他們會要求更多。

活用狄克生片語　Lesson 9 複習測驗

一、選擇題（請選出一個最適當的選項）

1. I hope my dreams _____.
   (A) become true　(B) come real　(C) come true　(D) come about

2. His new job _____ after he thought he had been hired.
   (A) fell through　(B) has fallen　(C) falling down　(D) fell around

3. You can trust him to _____ to all his promises.
   (A) hold good　(B) let go　(C) contain well　(D) keep right

4. Be careful not to _____ the assignment or the boss will be angry!
   (A) put out　(B) screw up　(C) hold on　(D) give in

二、翻譯填空

1. 在那幅畫所花的時間全白費了，因為都給這隻貓給毀了。
   The hours of work on that painting were all _____ _____ because the cat ruined it.

2. 這個月如果我們產品的銷量不足，我們未來的經營將瀕臨危險。
   The future of our business is _____ _____ if we don't sell enough products this month.

3. 這名士兵設法執行戰時下達給他的命令。
   The soldier tried to _____ _____ his orders during the battle.

三、中翻英

1. 設法不要屈服於朋友們的壓力而開始抽煙。
   _____

2. 當事情變得困難，你絕不應該放棄。
   _____

3. 批評（criticism）可能會有幫助，如果你沒有讓它給打敗。
   _____

Notes

Lesson 10

時間 Time

So you're going to move out of your parents' house.

From now on,[1] you will be in charge. You've just spent all day long[2] moving your things in, and so far,[3] your new place is looking good. Your friends were going to help, but they're never on time.[4]

Your new apartment is clean for the time being,[5] but you'll notice right away[6] that it won't stay clean for good.[7] You don't want to waste your time over[8] cleaning day after day,[9] but there's no one now, to pick up after you.

Wait a minute. This is your house, so your rules! If you don't want to clean, you don't have to!

When you do move out, you'll know it's time. But don't rush into independence, either. Take your time[10] and do it right.

Lesson 10

❶ from now on 從現在起

from（從）+ **now**（現在）+ **on**（持續地）= 從現在起；從今以後

解說　這裡的 now 可替換成特定的時間點，以表示「從（某個時間點）開始」，如：from then on（從那時起）、from that moment on（從那一刻起）。

例
- From now on, you can relax and let Tony do the driving.
  從現在起，你可以放輕鬆讓湯尼來開車。

似　starting (from) now/then/that moment 從現在／當時／那一刻起

---

❷ all day long 整天

all（全部的）+ **day**（一天）+ **long**（整段期間）= 整天

解說　這裡的 day 可替換成其他時間，以表示「整段期間」，如：all week/month/summer/year long（整個星期／月／夏天／年）。

例
- The balcony faces the south, so you get sunlight all day long.
  陽台朝向南方，所以整天都有充足的陽光。

---

❸ so far 到目前為止

so（如此）+ **far**（遠）= 相隔這麼遠；從過去一直到現在

| 時間 Time

| 解說 | 這個片語光看字面很容易誤解為「這麼遠」，so far 其實是指「到目前為止」，常用於現在完成式。

| 例 | • Jerry's company has been very successful so far.
傑瑞的公司到目前為止一直很成功。

| 同 | up to now 到目前為止

| 聯 | so far, so good（到目前為止，一切還好）

❹ on time　準時

on（在……）+ **time**（特定時間）＝ 在某特定時間點上

| 解說 | on time 是指按照約定或預定的時間，即「準時」之意。

| 例 | • You'd better be on time tomorrow; we have a meeting first thing in the morning.
你明天最好準時到，我們明天一早就要開會。

| 比 | in time 及時；遲早

❺ for the time being　目前；暫時

for（對……）+ **the time**（時間）+ **being**（現在的）＝ 針對現在這期間

| 解說 | being 僅在本片語才作形容詞用，意思是「現在的」。for the time being

Lesson 10

常用來暗示「目前」的情況只是暫時的,不會持續很久。

例
- We will get new books soon, but for the time being, we will use the old ones.
  我們很快就會拿到新書,不過目前我們先用舊書。

似　for now、for the moment、for the present 皆指「目前」。

---

❻ right away　立刻

right（作強調用）+ **away**（立刻）= 立刻

解說　right 作強調用,而此處的 away 則屬古老用法,意思是「立刻」。

例
- We'll get on that right away.
  我們會馬上處理。

同　right off、right off the bat、at once「立刻;馬上」

---

❼ for good　永久;永遠

for（為求得）+ **good**（利益）= 獲得所有利益

解說　原本完整的說法是 for good and all,其中的 good 作名詞用,意思是「利益」,因此 for good 便有「獲得所有利益;一勞永逸」之意,引申指「永久;永遠」。

| 例 | • The injury may keep him out of basketball for good.
這個傷可能讓他永遠無法再打籃球。 |

| 同 | forever 永久；永遠 |

❽ waste time over　浪費時間

waste（浪費）＋ **time**（時間）＋ **over**（關於）＝ 浪費時間在……之上

| 解説 | 其中的 over 常可用 on 代換，亦可省略 over 用「waste time + V-ing」句型來表示。 |

| 例 | • Why do I have to waste time over this?
我為什麼要浪費時間在這上面？
• I don't want to waste time arguing.
我不想浪費時間爭論。 |

| 註 | 亦可用 a waste of time (+ V-ing) 來表示。 |

| 比 | waste no time (in) V-ing 立刻著手進行…… |

❾ day after day　日復一日

day（一天）＋ **after**（一個接著一個）＋ **day**（一天）＝ 日復一日

| 解説 | day after day「日復一日」常指長期重複做著相同、單調或乏味的事物。 |

| 例 | • Jenny was tired of working nine to five day after day.
珍妮厭倦了每天朝九晚五的工作。 |

| 同 | day in day out 日復一日 |

❿ take one's time　別急；慢慢來

take（取得）+ **one's**（某人的）+ **time**（時間）= 某人會有時間做……

| 解說 | 「take one's time（+ V-ing）」常用來告訴某人「別急；慢慢來」，因為有的是時間。 |

| 例 | • Please take your time choosing what shoes to buy.
請慢慢挑選要買的鞋子。 |

活用狄克生片語　Lesson 10 複習測驗

一、選擇題（請選出一個最適當的選項）

1. _____, you must get out of bed in the morning at 6:30!
   (A) From now on   (B) Earlier than before   (C) Before now   (D) From here

2. It took them _____ to move into their new apartment.
   (A) all year long   (B) from now on   (C) right away   (D) all day long

3. I have earned about $5,000 _____ at my part-time job.
   (A) so long   (B) so far   (C) so away   (D) so near

4. He definitely needs a new watch because he's never _____.
   (A) at time   (B) by time   (C) on time   (D) from time

二、翻譯填空

1. 歡迎你待在這裡，暫時使用這部電腦。
   You are welcome to stay here and use the computer _____ _____ _____ _____.

2. 門鈴響了，他立刻跳起來去應門。
   The doorbell rang, and _____ _____ he jumped up to _____ it.

3. 她不喜歡她的手機，將要把它丟掉永遠不用。
   She hates her cell phone and is throwing it away _____ _____.

三、中翻英

1. 這是部愚蠢的電影，所以別浪費你的時間去看。

   _____

2. 日復一日，他早起送早報。

   _____

3. 最好慢慢來，把你的家庭作業給做好。

   _____

解答請參閱第260頁

Notes

Lesson 11

頻率 Frequency

When I was a child, I wanted nothing more than to be grown up. As soon as[1] I figured out I was grown up, I only wanted to still be a child.

At times[2] I think back to those innocent and carefree days. Every now and then[3] I wish I had done something different, but all along[4] I knew I would stand a chance[5] along with every other[6] kid if I just did my best and learned as much as I could.

Now, for once[7] I've accepted that I'll never be 13 again. Off and on[8] my mom still treats me like a kid and time and again,[9] I tell her I'm not a kid. Though once in a blue moon,[10] I secretly wish I still was that kid.

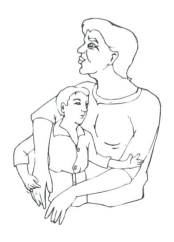

Lesson 11

❶ as soon as 一……立刻……

as（如同）＋ **soon**（很快地）＋ **as**（和……一樣）＝ 與……一樣快地

解說 第一個 as 作副詞用，第二個 as 則是連接詞；但 as soon as 並不是用來強調 as fast as「速度一樣快」，而是指「在某事發生後立刻……」。

例
- I'll see that he gets the message as soon as he returns.
  他一回來我就會把留言轉告給他。

❷ at times 有時；偶而

at（在……）＋ **times**（時候；期間）＝ 在有些時候

解說 為常見的頻率副詞片詞，意思是「有時；偶爾」。

例
- The kitten was fun, but at times it was very naughty.
  這隻小貓很有趣，但有時候很調皮。

似 sometimes、occasionally、every so often、(every) once in a while、(every) now and then「偶爾；有時」

❸ every now and then 有時；偶而

every（每）＋ **now**（現在）＋ **and**（和）＋ **then**（那時）＝ 現在和那時之間每隔一段時間

94

頻率 Frequency

| 解說 | 字面意思是「從那時到現在，每隔一陣子就會出現、發生」，也就是 every once in a while、from time to time「每隔一段時間」，切勿解讀為「經常；時常」，而是「有時；偶而」之意。 |

| 例 | • Everyone suffers from the blues every now and then.
每個人偶而都會感到憂鬱。 |

| 同 | every now and again 有時；偶而 |

| 註 | every so often 與 every now and then 同義，
千萬別解讀為「時常」。 |

❹ all along　一直；從一開始就
all（全部）**+ along**（沿著）**=** 一路從頭到尾

| 解說 | 用來表示事情發生「從頭到尾；一直；從一開始就」。 |

| 例 | • I should have known all along that you were lying.
我從一開始早該知道你在說謊。 |

| 同 | all the time、all the while、at all times「一直；始終」 |

❺ stand a chance　有希望；有可能
stand（佔了）**+ a chance**（一個機會）**=** 有成功的機會

Lesson 11

解說 stand 只有在本片語才作「擁有；佔了」解，而此處的 chance 是指 chance of success「成功的可能性」。stand a chance 是表示「有希望；有可能」，常以「stand a chance (of N. / V-ing)」句型出現。

例
- With Phil on the team, we stand a chance of winning the league championship.
  有菲爾在隊上，我們有機會奪得聯盟冠軍。

同 stand a hope 有希望；有可能

反 not stand a ghost of a chance 毫無希望

似 take a chance 碰運氣；冒風險

---

❻ every other   每隔……的；所有其他的

every（每）+ **other**（另一個的；其他的）= 每兩個中之一；所有其他的

解說 every other 由於解析方式的不同，而有兩個完全不一樣的意思，究竟是「每兩個中之一；每隔……的」還是「所有其他的」，必須視上下文而定。

例
- He visits his parents every other weekend.
  他每隔一個星期去探望他的父母。

- Our basketball team defeated every other team.
  我們籃球隊打敗了所有其他隊伍。

頻率 Frequency

❼ for once　就這麼一次；僅此一次

for（針對）＋ **once**（一次）＝ 就這麼一次

解說　(just) for once 常以無奈或負面的語氣出現，表示希望某事能發生「至少一次；就算一次也好」。

例
- It would be nice of you to remember our wedding anniversary, for once.
  你就算只記得我們的結婚紀念日一次也好。

---

❽ off and on　斷斷續續

off（關）＋ **and**（又）＋ **on**（開）＝ 開開關關

解說　off and on 亦可寫成 on and off，用來形容事物「斷斷續續」，猶如電器開關「開開關關」。

例
- The light blinked off and on.
  燈光忽明忽滅。

聯　on and on 不停地；不斷地

❾ time and again　屢次;一再地

time（一次）＋ **and**（又）＋ **again**（再一次）＝ 一次又一次

解說　形容事物「屢次;一再地」經常發生。

例
- Time and again, Steve was late for class.
  史提夫上課一再遲到。

同　again and again、time after time、over and over「屢次;再三地」

❿ once in a blue moon　很少;不常

once（一次）＋ **in**（在……時候）＋ **a blue moon**（藍色月亮）
＝ 有一次出現藍色月亮

解說　blue moon「藍月」原本是天文學上的一個專有名詞,指同一曆月的第二次滿月,但顯然被古人所誤用,因為藍月並非真的很罕見,有時因為天候的關係也可以看到真正的藍色月亮。如今,once in a blue moon 常用來形容事情只在非常偶然或罕見的情況下才發生。

例
- We eat out once in a blue moon.
  我們很少出去外面吃。

活用狄克生片語　Lesson 11 複習測驗

一、選擇題（請選出一個最適當的選項）

1. 1. _____ I decided to come to Taiwan, I bought my plane ticket online.
   (A) As fast as　(B) As soon on　(C) As soon as　(D) As early as

2. _____, I like to pretend that I'm a famous singer on television.
   (A) At times　(B) On times　(C) Before times　(D) By times

3. My mother calls and talks to me about getting married _____.
   (A) very soon　(B) every now and then　(C) all along　(D) for once

4. Tommy tried to trick me, but he failed because _____ I knew what he was doing!
   (A) as soon as　(B) all around　(C) all along　(D) as early as

二、翻譯填空

1. 我男朋友不時會帶我去很好的餐廳吃晚餐。
   _____ _____ _____, my boyfriend will take me to a very nice restaurant for dinner.

2. 除了史黛西以外，所有其他音樂會的舞者都很棒。
   _____ _____ dancer in the concert was great except for Stacy.

3. 很罕見地，這位忙錄的老闆請了很長的假充電休息。
   _____ _____ _____ _____ _____, the busy boss takes a very long vacation to feel refreshed.

三、中翻英

1. 她是個好學生，但她知道她沒希望進入哈佛大學。

2. 她一再試著減肥，但卻無法停止吃甜甜圈。

3. 嘿，就這麼一次，我考試得了A+。

Notes

Lesson 12

順序 Order

Sooner or later[1] everybody gets into trouble. But for Chad, it seemed his troubles lined up one after another.[2] We used to take turns[3] riding my motorcycle to school. We took turns wearing my black leather jacket, gloves, and motorcycle helmet. One day, everything got mixed up.[4]

It was Chad's turn to ride. I was about to[5] get on the bus, when all of a sudden,[6] he came roaring around the corner. At first[7] I thought he was just playing, but before long[8] I could see something was wrong. Two police motorcycles sped around the corner after him.

He had run a stop sign and the police mistook him for a motorcycle gang member. After some time it was at last[9] sorted out. In the long run,[10] I think he better stay away from motorcycles all together.

Lesson 12

❶ sooner or later　遲早

sooner（快一點）＋ or（或）＋ later（慢一點）＝ 遲早

解說　用來表示雖然不知道什麼時候，但可以肯定某事將來「遲早」會發生。

例
- I think your girlfriend will find out sooner or later.
  我想你女朋友遲早會發現。

❷ one after another　一個接一個

one（一個）＋ after（在……後面）＋ another（另一個）＝ 一個接一個

解說　常指不好的事情「一個接一個；接踵而來」。

例
- Today I have three different exams one after another.
  今天我連續有三個不同考試。

同　one after the other　一個接一個

似　one thing after another（壞事、惡運等）接踵而來

❸ take turns　輪流

take（採取行動）＋ turns（輪流）＝ 採輪流的方式

順序 Order

解説 take turns 是指「輪流」做事情，其後通常加 V-ing，但在英式英文中亦可用不定詞 to do，例如：We need to take turns to cook.（我們必須輪流煮飯。）

例
- We took turns driving on the way to Taipei.
  我們一路輪流開車到台北。

可分開片語

❹ mix up 搞混；充分混合

mix（混合）+ **up**（完全地）= 完全混合

解説 mix up 除指「充分混合」，亦可表示將事物「搞混；弄混淆」。

例
- I often mix up the steps that our math teacher shows us in class.
  我常會把數學老師上課時教我們的步驟搞混。

註1 亦可用被動語態「be/get mixed up（about + 事物）」來表示，例如：
- The new teacher kept getting the students' names mixed up.
  那位新老師一直搞不清楚學生們的名字。

註2 但「be/get mixed up + in + 事物」是表示「捲入、牽扯入某事物」。

註3 而「be/get mixed up + with + 人」則表示「與某人廝混、鬼混」。

103

Lesson 12

❺ about to　即將；正要

about（有……打算）＋ **to**（要）＝ 剛要做；正想做

解說　此處的 about 為形容詞，意思是「有……的企圖或打算」。about to 是指某人「正要」做某事，或某事「即將」發生。

例
- I'm just about to leave, so we'll have to talk tomorrow.
  我馬上就要走了，所以我們明天再談吧。
- Please fasten your seat belts; the plane is about to take off.
  請繫上安全帶，飛機要起飛了。

似　on the point / verge of ＋ V-ing / N. 即將

比　will 指「未來的任何一個時間點」；(just) about to 則指「即將」

---

❻ all of a sudden　突然

all（作強調用）＋ **of**（在……之前）＋ **a sudden**（無預期地發生）
＝ 比預期發生的還要早；突然

解說　sudden 為名詞，指「事情無預期地發生」。all of a sudden 常指事情發生得「很突然」。

例
- All of a sudden, he was surrounded by police.
  突然間，他被警察包圍了。

同　all at once 突然

順序 Order

❼ at first　起初

at（在）+ **first**（最初；開始）= 起初

解說　at first 意思等於 at / in the beginning「起初；一開始」。

例
- I didn't like her at first, but we eventually became best friends.
起初我並不喜歡她，但最後我們成了好朋友。

反　at last 最後；終於

❽ before long　很快；不久

before（在……之前）+ **long**（長久）= 不會很久

解說　before long 為副詞片語，意思等於 soon「很快；不久」。

例
- The company has had a successful year, and before long, it could become one of the leaders in the industry.
這家公司過去這年很成功，不久可能會成為業界的翹楚。

❾ at last　最後；終於

at（在）+ **last**（最後）= 最後

解說　at last 意思等於 in the end「最後」。

例
- At last I can rest and watch some soap operas.
  我終於可以休息，看看肥皂劇了。

反　at first 起初

---

❿ in the long run　終究；到最後

in（在）+ **the long**（長的）+ **run**（跑步）= 一路跑到最後

解說　原指跑者在賽跑中一路跑到最後，引申指「終究；到最後」。

例
- Selling our products at such a low price is not good for the company in the long run.
  我們的產品用這麼低的價格販售，對公司而言並非長久之計。

反　in the short run 短時間內；短期內

活用狄克生片語　Lesson 12 複習測驗

一、選擇題（請選出一個最適當的選項）

1. _____, you're going to have to get out of bed.
   (A) All of a sudden　(B) So far　(C) At first　(D) Sooner or later

2. The children got off the school bus _____.
   (A) one after another　(B) one before another　(C) one along another　(D) one by another

3. I suggest we _____ cleaning our apartment each week, OK?
   (A) try turns　(B) take turns　(C) do turns　(D) make turns

4. Oops, I made a cake yesterday and got the recipe _____!
   (A) mixed up　(B) mixed down　(C) mixed on　(D) mixed over

二、翻譯填空

1. 我好朋友來看我，我這時正好要出門上班。
   My best friend came over to visit me just as I was _____ _____ leave for work.

2. 我電腦很快就不用了，之後你就可以用來打電腦遊戲。
   I will be finished using the computer _____ _____ and then you can play games on it.

3. 起初我不知道那男人是誰，但後來得知他是我表哥。
   I didn't know who that man was _____ _____, but I learned he was my cousin.

三、中翻英

1. 昨天我正在公園散步時，突然間便開始下雨。
   _____

2. 我們在雨中等了二十分鍾，但最後巴士終於來了。
   _____

3. 現在努力讀大學，到最後將有助於找到好一點的工作。
   _____

Notes

Lesson 13

因果關係 Cause & Effect

Track 13

Everybody is asking for[1] something cute these days.

As a result,[2] many fast food restaurants and convenient stores are turning out[3] dolls of cute kitties, doggies, or anything that has to do with[4] cute animals in popular movies or cartoons.

Now that[5] this has happened, it has led to[6] many kids in high school asking for more and more cute stuff. In fact,[7] many kids are crazy about collecting these cute toys and putting them on their book bags and clothes.

Every time a new promotion takes place,[8] people stand for hours in line and wait for the newest, cutest doll. Sometimes arguments break out[9] because people cut in line.

My parents won't let me do that. While everyone is standing in line, I study. No wonder[10] my test scores are the best in my class.

❶ ask for　要求;活該

ask（要求）＋ for（為得到……）＝ 要求得到

解說　「ask for + 事物」是指「要求某事物」；「ask for + 人」是指「求見某人」。

例
- Maggie realized the opportunity to ask for a pay raise had passed her by.
  瑪姬知道自己錯失了要求加薪的機會。

註　常以句型「be asking for + it/trouble」表示「活該;自找麻煩」。

聯　ask for the moon 奢求不可得之物或不可能之事

---

❷ as a result　結果;因此

as（作為）＋ a（一個）＋ result（結果）＝ 結果

解說　as a result 作副詞用，屬於正式用語，除單獨使用外，亦常以句型「as a result + of + 事物」表示「由於某事物所造成的結果」。

例
- The world is getting warmer. As a result, weather is becoming more extreme.
  全球逐漸暖化，因此，氣候變得越來越不尋常。

似　because of（因為）、owing to（由於）

因果關係 Cause & Effect

❸ turn out　結果變成；生產；出席

turn（轉變）**+ out**（顯現出來；向外）**= 轉變產生；外出**

解說　turn out 有許多不同意思，在此僅介紹以下三種：

1.「產生……的結果」
2.「生產（產品）」（為可分開片語）
3.「外出；出席」

例
- Learning Spanish turned out to be harder than I thought.
  學西班牙語結果比我想像中還難。

- The factory turns out 1500 units a day.
  該工廠每天可生產一千五百件。

- Thousands of fans turned out for the singer's concert.
  數千位歌迷出席這位歌手的演唱會。

註1　turn out 作「產生……的結果；結果原來是……」解時，可用的句型相當多，主要分為以下兩類：

1.「turn out + 副詞／形容詞／不定詞／that 子句」
2.「turn out + to be 名詞／形容詞」

註2　turn out 作「生產（產品）」解時，為可分開片語。

❹ have to do with　與……有關

have（有）＋ **to do with**（與……有關）＝ 與……有關

解說　「have to do with + 受詞」是指與後面的受詞「有關」。

例
- I had nothing to do with the crime; my hands are clean!
  我和那個案件一點關係也沒有，我是清白的！

註　常可在 have 和 to do with 間插入修飾語來形容關聯性有多大，如：have much/something/nothing to do with（有很大／有些／沒有關係）。

---

❺ now that　既然；因為

now（既然）＋ **that**（……事）＝ 既然

解說　now that 表示「由於；既然」，為連接詞，後面必須接子句。

例
- Now that we know it won't rain, we can go on a picnic.
  既然知道不會下雨，我們就可以去郊遊。

註　now that you mention it 常用來表示自己以前並未注意到或想到某事，直到「你現在提起才注意到或想到」。

- Now that you mention it, I do need a vacation.
  經你這麼一提，我實在需要休個長假。

因果關係 Cause & Effect

❻ lead to　導致；通往

lead（引導）＋ to（向）＝ 導致；通往

解說　lead to 的 to 為介系詞而非不定詞，後面要接 V-ing 或名詞。

例
- Smoking leads to cancer.
  抽煙會引起癌症。
- All roads lead to Rome.
  條條道路通羅馬。
- Drinking and driving will lead to losing your license.
  酒醉駕駛將導致被吊銷駕照。

似　result in、bring about、cause「導致；造成；引起」

❼ in fact　事實上；其實

in（在……方面）＋ fact（事實）＝ 事實上

解說　in fact 主要用來「作強調」或指出與前面所說的「有差別」。

例
- I don't like cooking, in fact, I hate cooking.
  我不喜歡做菜，事實上，我討厭做菜。

似　as a matter of fact 事實上；實際上

❽ take place　舉行；發生

take（佔有）+ **place**（場地）= 佔有場地進行

解說　take place 意指「（活動；會議等）舉行；發生」，主詞為事物，後面可接地點或時間。

例
- The rock festival took place at Fulong beach from August 12 to 14.
  搖滾音樂祭於八月十二日至十四日在福隆海水浴場舉行。

似　be held 舉行
- Our class reunion will be held in Taipei this summer.
  我們同學會將在今年夏天於台北舉行。

❾ break out　爆發；發生

break（破裂）+ **out**（向外）= 爆發

解說　break out 常指事物「突然發生」。

例
- A fire broke out on the third floor.
  三樓發生了火災。

衍　名詞 outbreak 是指疾病、戰爭等「爆發」，常以「outbreak of + 事物」表示。

註　「burst／break out + crying／laughing」是指「突然哭了起來／笑了起來」。

因果關係 Cause & Effect

⑩ no wonder 難怪

no（沒有任何）＋ **wonder**（驚訝）＝ 不足為奇

解說　no wonder 後面常接 that 子句（其中的 that 常可省略），以表示「難怪；不足為奇」。

例
- The battery's dead; no wonder my cellphone won't work!
  電池沒電了，難怪我的手機不能用！

註　亦常以「(it's) little/small/no wonder (that)」句型表示「難怪；不足為奇」。

115

活用狄克生片語　Lesson 13 複習測驗

一、選擇題（請選出一個最適當的選項）

1. I can't understand what that foreigner is _____ right now.
   (A) asking for　(B) asking of　(C) asking over　(D) asking at

2. I missed the bus and _____, I was late for work.
   (A) at a result　(B) for a result　(C) of the result　(D) as a result

3. That factory is _____ hundreds of new cars each month.
   (A) turning on　(B) turning about　(C) turning out　(D) turning up

4. I don't understand what my problem _____ you!
   (A) has to do with　(B) has to do at　(C) has to do on　(D) has to do from

二、翻譯填空

1. 既然我已大學畢業，我將要去找份新工作。
   _____ _____ I've graduated from college, I'm going to look for a new job.

2. 他被升職，薪資也因而高出許多。
   His promotion at work _____ _____ a much higher salary.

3. 你晚餐後喝了兩杯咖啡，難怪你睡不著。
   _____ _____ you can't sleep, you had two cups of coffee after dinner!

三、中翻英

1. 你知道瑪丹娜（Madonna）明年倫敦的演唱會何時舉辦？

   _____

2. 昨天在學校我看到我兩個朋友之間爆發打架衝突。

   _____

3. 我根本不認識他，事實上，我跟他今晚才第一次見面。

   _____

Lesson 14

財富 Wealth

It would be great to be rich!

If you are rich, you can buy anything you want and everything is a steal.[1] While other people are trying to cut corners[2] and save money, you can live it up[3] and do anything you want.

You could sleep all day and shop all night. You could buy up[4] all the things you like: perfume, all the hot brands, fancy cars—you name it. You could buy so many things the shop owners would complain they are sold out[5] of all the fashionable things.

When you are well-off,[6] you don't have to think about how you can earn a living[7] because your only job is to keep getting richer and richer. While others are trying to get out from under[8] all the debt they have, you can sit by the pool and spend the whole day dreaming about things you can buy.

No, you know what? I really don't think you'd be better off[9] rich. Money can't buy satifaction and the love of family and friends.

I wouldn't trade in[10] my life for all the gold in the world. I'm already rich in my heart!

Lesson 14

❶ a steal 非常便宜

a（一件）＋ steal（偷來的東西）＝ 一件偷來的東西

解說　誇張地形容物品簡直像是偷來的一樣「極為便宜」。

例
- This dress is a steal at $100.
  這件洋裝賣一百元實在很便宜。

❷ cut corners 節省；偷工減料

cut（剪）＋ corners（轉角）＝ 貼近轉角走

解說　原指轉彎時盡可能地貼近轉角邊緣，以縮短所需走的路程，如今用來形容做事時採最省時、省事或省錢的方法，常指「貪圖簡便；偷工減料」。

例
- The company started to cut corners to save money and quality dropped dramatically.
  該公司為了省錢而開始偷工減料，品質便急遽下降。
- If you cut corners now, you will only regret it in the future.
  如果你現在做事貪圖簡便，將來只會後悔。

❸ live it up 盡情享樂；花費闊綽

live（生活）＋ it（它）＋ up（完全地）＝ 盡情享受生活

財富 Wealth

解說 為口語用法，指「盡情享樂」，常含有「揮霍；盡情放縱」之意。

例
- It is your birthday, so you should live it up: eat at an expensive restaurant, see a movie . . .
今天是你生日，你應該盡情享受一下：去昂貴的餐廳吃飯、看場電影……

比 live up to (something) 則指「遵行（某事物）；達到（要求或期望）」，例如：

- Jill made a promise to her father, and she wanted to live up to that promise.
吉兒對她父親許過承諾，她想達成那個承諾。

---

❹ buy up　全部買下；大量收購　　*可分開片語*

buy（買）＋ **up**（完全地）＝ 全部買下

解說 除指「全部買下；買斷」，亦可指「大量收購」。

例
- The company bought up the entire piece of land surrounding the office building.
該公司買下辦公大樓周圍整片土地。

Lesson 14

❺ sell out　賣完；銷售一空　　可分開片語

sell（賣）＋ **out**（完全地）＝ 全部賣完

解說　指「銷售一空」，亦常以「sell out of + 貨品」句型表示某貨品已全部賣完。

例
- The singer's new album took Europe by storm and all her concert dates sold out.
  該歌手的新專輯風靡歐洲，其演唱會所有場次的門票均已銷售一空。

---

❻ be well-off　生活富裕

be（是）＋ **well-off**（富裕的）＝ 生活富裕

解說　亦可說成 be well off，意思是「生活富裕」。

例
- Susan's family is well-off.
  蘇珊家裡生活富裕。

似　be well-to-do 富裕；有錢

反　be badly off 貧困

比　be better off 除指「更有錢」外，亦可指「情況好轉」，而「be better off + V-ing」則常用來勸告別人「最好⋯⋯」。

財富 Wealth

❼ earn a living　賺錢謀生

earn（賺）＋ **a living**（生計）＝ 賺取生活費

解說　這裡的 earn 也可以用 make 取代，常以「earn/make a living + (by) V-ing」句型出現，表示「以……維生」。

例
- He earns a living as a magician.
= He earns a living doing tricks.
  他以變魔術維生。

似　「V. + for a living」「從事……維生」，例如：
- Mary is a fortune-teller; she tells fortunes for a living.
  瑪莉是個算命師，她以算命維生。

❽ get out from under　擺脫負擔

get out（擺脫）＋ **from**（從）＋ **under**（承受）＝ 擺脫……的負擔

解說　這個片語可單獨使用，也可以在後面加上所承受的負擔，常指「擺脫債務或工作上的負擔」。

例
- How can I get out from under this debt?
  我要如何才能還清這筆債務？

Lesson 14

❾ be better off　情況好轉；更有錢

be better（較好）+ **off**（處於……情況的）= 處於較好的狀況

【解說】off 在此作形容詞用，意思是「處於……情況的」；be better off 除指「情況好轉」外，亦可指「更有錢」。

【例】
- Sarah is better off since she moved to Japan.
  莎拉自從搬到日本後，生活情況便有好轉。

【註】「be better off + V-ing」則常用來勸告別人「最好……」，例如：
- The weather is so bad, we are better off staying at home.
  天氣這麼糟，我們最好還是待在家裡。

---

❿ trade in　以舊品折價買新品　（可分開片語）

trade（交易）+ **in**（在裡面）= 包括到交易裡面

【解說】trade in 意思是「以舊品折價買新品」，而 trade-in 則為其名詞形式。

【例】
- We're giving our customers a chance to trade in their old phones for $50 off the new Phone Extra.
  我們目前提供機會給顧客以舊機折抵五十元換購新的 Phone Extra 電話。

【註】trade in 亦可指「做……的生意或買賣」，但這時為不可分片語，例如：trade in oil / textiles（做石油／紡織品生意）。

活用狄克生片語　Lesson 14 複習測驗

一、選擇題（請選出一個最適當的選項）

1. You got a great deal on those shoes, what a _____!
   (A) spin　　　　(B) standard　　　(C) steal　　　　(D) solution

2. I know you want to work faster, but you can't _____.
   (A) cut corners　(B) tie corners　　(C) bend corners　(D) stretch corners

3. My roommate stays out late every night and _____.
   (A) lives it high　(B) lives it up　　(C) lives it down　(D) lives it around

4. During a sale at the department store, the shoppers quickly _____ all the bargains.
   (A) bought in　　(B) bought out　　(C) bought up　　(D) bought down

二、翻譯填空

1. 我有輛很棒的車，我才不要換那部爛車。
   I have a great car and would never _____ it _____ for that _____!

2. 我老闆很富有，他計畫四十五歲退休。
   My boss is very _____ and plans to _____ when he's 45.

3. 我三十歲的弟弟不想賺錢謀生，所以他現在還跟我父母住在一起。
   My 30-year-old brother doesn't want to _____ _____ _____, so he's still living with my parents.

三、中翻英

1. 想要有成功的人生，你就必須擺脫沈重的負債。
   _____

2. 假如你多讀書少玩樂，在學校表現就會好轉。
   _____

3. 最熱門的電腦遊戲總是最先賣完。
   _____

Notes

Lesson 15

接洽聯絡 Contacting

Track 15

It's tough being a salesperson.

I'm busy all the time talking to people. If I'm not making presentations, I'm kicking around[1] new ideas with colleagues.

Every day I have to get in touch with[2] new clients. Sometimes they aren't very nice to me. I call them up[3] and tell them about the interesting products our company has. Before I can finish, they hang up.[4] Or maybe while I'm talking they tell me to hold on[5] and never come back to the phone.

When I meet with them and try to talk over[6] the wonderful services our company has, they cut in[7] and ask me to lower the price. That is, by the way,[8] if I get to meet them at all. Many times they say they want to meet me but leave the dates open[9] and never decide.

So the next time you talk to a salesperson, imagine being in my shoes[10] for a moment.

❶ kick around （非正式）討論

kick（踢）＋ **around**（到處）＝ 到處踢

解說　kick around 為口語用法，引申指對想法、議題等進行「（非正式）討論」。

例
- We need to get everyone together and kick it around for a while.
  我們大家得聚在一起討論一下。

似　kick about（非正式）討論

註　受詞若為人，則指「對某人態度惡劣；欺負某人」

❷ get in touch with　與……聯絡

get（取得）＋ **in touch**（接觸）＋ **with**（和）＝ 與……取得聯絡

解說　get in touch with 是指以通訊或書信等方式「與某人聯絡」。

例
- Can I have your cell phone number in case I need to get in touch with you?
  能不能給我你的手機號碼，以防萬一必須和你聯絡？

聯　keep/stay in touch (with someone) 與某人保持聯絡

反　lose touch with 與……失去聯絡

接洽聯絡 Contacting

❸ call up　打電話　可分開片語

call（打電話；喚起）＋ up（出現；發生）＝ 打電話給；使回想起

[解說]　「打電話」除可單獨用 call 一個字外，亦常和 up 連用。此外，call up 亦可指「喚起（記憶）；使回想起」。

[例]
- I'll call you up this week to give you my final decision.
  這個禮拜我會打電話給你，告訴你我最後的決定。

[同]　give someone a call 打電話給某人

❹ hang up　掛斷電話；懸掛　可分開片語

hang（懸掛）＋ up（上去）＝ 掛上去

[解說]　hang up 除指「掛斷電話」外，亦可指「懸掛」東西。

[例]
- Jenny hung up on Mary after they had an argument.
  珍妮和瑪莉發生爭吵後，掛了她電話。

- Where should I hang up my jacket?
  我的夾克該掛到哪裡？

[聯]　「hang up + on 人」掛某人電話

❺ hold on　稍候；抓緊；堅持

hold（持續；抓住）＋ **on**（繼續）＝ 繼續維持；抓緊

[解說] hold on 主要有以下三種意思：(1)「稍候」 (2)「抓緊」 (3)「堅持下去」。

[例]
- Could you hold on a moment?
  你能不能稍等一下？

- The young boy held on to his mother tightly after he heard the loud sound.
  小男孩聽到這巨大的聲響後，便緊緊抓住他母親。

- If you hold on to your dreams, you will succeed.
  如果你堅持你的夢想，就會成功。

[註1] hold on a second/minute/moment 表示請對方「等一下」，也可只說 hold on。

[註2] 作「抓緊」解時，常以「hold on to ＋ 受詞」表示「抓緊……」。

❻ talk over　討論；商量　（可分開片語）

talk（說話）＋ **over**（關於）＝ 對……進行討論

[解說] 常用來表示對問題、計畫等進行「商討」。

[例]
- I need to talk it over with my wife.
  我必須和我太太討論一下。

接洽聯絡 **Contacting**

同　discuss 討論；商量

---

❼ cut in　插嘴；插隊

cut（切斷）＋ **in**（向裡面）＝ 切斷進入

解說　cut in 主要指「插嘴」或「插隊」，意思可依上下文或當時情境作判斷。

例
- Don't cut in! I haven't finished speaking.
  別插嘴！我還沒講完。
- As he walked into the burger bar, someone cut in front of him.
  當他走進漢堡店時，有人插隊到他前面。

似　interrupt 插嘴

註　cut in line 插隊（為美式用法）

---

❽ by the way　順便一提

by（藉由）＋ **the way**（此路；此法）＝ 順道；藉由此法

解說　常置於句首，用來改變話題，可譯作「順便一提；對了；可是」。

例
- By the way, is that a new jacket? It's lovely.
  對了，那件夾克是新的嗎？很好看。

Lesson 15

聯 在簡訊或電子郵件中可簡寫為 BTW。

註 由於 way 亦有「方法」之意，因此，by the way 若在句中出現時，也有可能是指「藉由此法」。

---

❾ leave open　暫緩決定　*可分開片語*

leave（讓……處於）+ **open**（開放的）= 讓……處於開放的狀態

解說 leave open 除實際指「讓……開著」，如：leave the door open；亦可抽象地表示「暫緩決定」，好讓將來有更多選擇的空間。

例
- We should leave our options open until we get all the information.
  未拿到所有資料之前，我們應先暫緩決定。

---

❿ be in (someone's) shoes　站在某人的立場

be in（穿著）+ **someone's**（某人的）+ **shoes**（鞋子）
= 穿著某人的鞋子

解說 此處的 shoes 是用來比喻某人的「立場」，因此亦可說成 be in (someone's) place「站在某人的立場」。

例
- Put yourself in my shoes; I had no choice.
  你站在我的立場想想，我別無選擇。

一式搞定狄克生片語 Lesson 15 複習測驗

一、選擇題（請選出一個最適當的選項）

1. If you have time, I'd like to _____ an idea with you.
   (A) kick around (B) kick by (C) kick over (D) kick a little

2. He doesn't have a cell phone, so it's hard to get _____ him.
   (A) in touch around (B) in touch on (C) in touch for (D) in touch with

3. You don't understand the situation, you should try _____.
   (A) living in my place (B) being in my shoes
   (C) acting in my place (D) living in my shoes

4. I wish I could say what I need to, but she always _____ and doesn't let me finish my sentence.
   (A) cuts at (B) cuts on (C) cuts away (D) cuts in

二、翻譯填空

1. 我必須跟我房東談合約。
   I need to _____ _____ my contract with my landlord.

2. 我今晚忙著寫家庭作業。對了，麻煩把我借你的書還給我好嗎？
   I'm busy tonight with homework. _____ _____ _____, will you return the book I lent you?

3. 我正計畫下個月二十號開個派對，所以請將那天空下來等我作好決定。
   I'm planning a party on the 20th next month, so please _____ _____ _____ _____ until I decide.

三、中翻英

1. 當銷售員打電話到家裡，人們通常會掛他們電話。
   _____

2. 有時小孩子會告訴來電者稍候，然後就忘記告訴大人有人打電話來。
   _____

3. 如果你覺得寂寞，就打電話給我，我就會過來。
   _____

Notes

Lesson 16

爭執 Argument

I normally don't speak ill of[1] my friends, but Brian got me really upset the other day.

He asked me to do his term paper for him. I told him to give me a break.[2] I hadn't even done my own, yet. He got a little angry. Well okay, I won't beat around the bush.[3] He got really mad, so I told him I would do it.

Did you ever hear of[4] a friend doing that? I don't like to find fault with[5] people, but I started to feel like he was using me. I told him I wanted to back out,[6] but he said he was going to report me to the dean at school if I did. As if I had brought it up in the first place!

Well, I went to the dean to clear things up.[7] The dean called me down[8] for getting involved. Plus, now I'm in trouble for talking back to[9] him! Search me,[10] but I think Brian got to the dean somehow, too!

Lesson 16

❶ speak ill of　說人壞話

speak（說）＋**ill**（壞）＋**of**（關於）＝說人壞話

解說　speak ill of 也就是 say bad things about「說人壞話」之意。

例
- Craig spoke ill of Mandy's mother just to get a reaction.
  克瑞格說曼蒂母親壞話，只是為了看看有什麼反應。

反　speak well of 說人好話

---

❷ give (someone) a break　放……一馬；饒了……吧

give（給）＋**someone**（某人）＋**a break**（一個機會）＝給某人一個機會

解說　除了字面意思「要求給一個機會」外，常用來表示不要批評、為難某人，就「放某人一馬；饒了某人吧」。

例
- Give Paul a break. He only started at the company last week.
  就放保羅一馬吧，他上星期才剛來上班。

聯　give me a break 是俚語用法，意指「饒了我吧；別再煩我；別尋我開心」，帶有半開玩笑的語氣，當有人作弄你或不斷煩你時，就可用這句話來回應對方。

爭執 Argument

❸ beat around the bush　拐彎抹角

beat（拍打）＋ around（在周圍）＋ the bush（灌木叢）

＝ 在灌木叢四周拍打

解說　原指打獵時，在灌木叢四周拍打，以獵取獵物。如今，常引申指「拐彎抹角；支吾其詞」。

例
- Not wanting to tell Bill what happened, Tom kept beating around the bush.
  湯姆一直支吾其詞，不想告訴比爾發生了什麼事。

❹ hear of　聽說；得知

hear（聽）＋ of（關於）＝ 聽到關於……

解說　hear of 意思是「聽說；得知」，常用於否定句及疑問句。

例
- I'm sorry. I've never heard of that artist.
  抱歉，我從未聽過那位藝術家。

註　片語 not hear of it 是指「聽不進去；不聽從」，例如：

- I wanted to pay but my wife wouldn't hear of it.
  我要付錢，但我太太就是不聽我的。

比　hear from 是指「接到（某人）來信或來電」或「得到（某人）的消息」。

135

Lesson 16

❺ find fault with　挑毛病；找碴

find（找到）＋ **fault**（過錯）＋ **with**（關於）＝ 找出……的過失

解說　「find fault with ＋ 人／事物」是指刻意「挑毛病；找碴」。

例
- He's always finding fault with me.
  他老愛找我碴。

❻ back out　退出；食言

back（後退）＋ **out**（向外）＝ 退出

解說　這是一個口語用法，常用來比喻對計畫、約定等「打退堂鼓；食言」。

例
- I am not going to back out of my promise.
  我不會違背我的承諾。

註　常以「back out ＋ of ＋ 受詞」表示「從……退出」或「不履行……」。

❼ clear up　澄清；清理　（可分開片語）

clear（清除）＋ **up**（完全地）＝ 清理；澄清

解說　clear up 字面意思是指「清潔整理」，但亦可抽象地表示除去疑慮作「澄清」。

爭執 Argument

例
- I believe this will clear up some of the questions we had.
  我相信這將釐清我們之前的一些問題。

註 clear up 亦可指天氣「放晴」，但要注意，此時為不可分開片語。

- The sky cleared up.
  天空放晴了。

❽ call down　責罵　可分開片語

call（大聲叫）+ **down**（向下）=　貶低

解說　這是一個美式俚語，指「責罵」，常以「call + 人 + down」的形式出現。

例
- The teacher called me down in front of the class.
  老師在全班面前責罵我。

似　reprimand、scold「責罵；譴責；斥責」

❾ talk back to　頂嘴

talk（說）+ **back**（返回）+ **to**（向）=　頂嘴

解說　talk back 即有「頂嘴」之意，當後面有接受詞時，才須用「talk back to + 人」來表達「向……頂嘴」。

例
- You shouldn't talk back to your parents.
  你不該頂撞你的父母。

Lesson 16

❿ search me　　我不知道；問倒我

search（搜索）**+ me**（我）**=** 搜我吧

[解說] 這是個口語用法,藉由「就算把我全身搜遍了也找不到」來比喻「我不知道;問倒我」。

[例] • "Where's your mom?" "Search me!"
「你媽在哪?」「我哪知道!」

[似] **beats me** 這可難倒我了;我不知道

活用狄克生片語　Lesson 16 複習測驗

一、選擇題（請選出一個最適當的選項）

1. It's not polite to _____ anyone, especially your family and friends.
   (A) speak ill of　(B) speak right of　(C) talk nicely of　(D) talk around

2. _____ , I can't help you cheat on the test.
   (A) Give me a turn (B) Let me have a rest (C) Show me a sign (D) Give me a break

3. He's very direct and never _____ when he has something to say.
   (A) jogs around the subject　　(B) beats around the bush
   (C) runs around the tree　　　(D) hits around the mark

4. Did you ever _____ a 10-year-old going to college?
   (A) see about`　(B) know on　(C) hear of　(D) listen to

二、翻譯填空

1. 那女孩老愛挑別人毛病，卻從未想過自己也有錯。
   That girl loves to _____ _____ _____ other people, but never thinks she's wrong, herself.

2. 你現在取消明年去歐洲度假並不會太遲。
   It's not too late to _____ _____ of your vacation to Europe next year.

3. 當你有誤會，最好試著與對方把事情澄清。
   When you have a misunderstanding, it's best to try to _____ _____ _____ with the other person.

三、中翻英

1. 湯尼在學校惹了麻煩，並被他老師責罵。

   _____

2. 身為小孩，頂撞大人是很不禮貌的，尤其是你的父母。

   _____

3. 我哪知道，我想像不出你今天早上可能把鑰匙給放在哪裡。

   _____

Notes

Lesson 17

工作 On the Job

A couple of weeks ago Terry asked me if I'd cover for[1] him on his job so he could go to the beach. I'm not exactly cut out for[2] manual labor, but I'd told him I'd be on duty[3] in his place. He said gardening was really easy and I'd be able to take over[4] his job with no problem.

Usually he spreads new grass seed at this time, but he said I could let that slide[5] and just carry on[6] with cutting the grass.

I got to the first gardening site at 6:00 a.m. all ready to begin my new job. I set up[7] the mower and other equipment. When I started up the power lawn mower the owner came running out yelling at me that he wouldn't stand for[8] being woken up at 6 a.m. He said he would lay me off[9] until Terry came back to work. Fired my first day!

I was discouraged, so I called it a day[10] and went to the beach to meet up with Terry.

Lesson 17

❶ cover for　暫代；掩護

cover（掩護）**+ for**（為）**=** 為……掩護

解說　在工作上，cover for 是指某人因生病、出差等原因不在，於是請同仁「暫代」其職務；在生活中，cover for 則常指為避免某人受到懲罰而為其「（說謊）掩護」。

例
- Brenda will cover for Mike while he is on vacation.
  邁克休假期間將由布蘭達暫代。
- If mom asks where I am, will you cover for me?
  如果媽問我在哪裡，替我掩護一下好嗎？

❷ be cut out for　很適合；能勝任

be（是）**+ cut out**（剪裁）**+ for**（為）**=** 為……所量身訂做

解說　be cut out for 是用來形容人「很適合」某項工作、事務等，就像衣服量身訂做一樣的合身。

例
- You're really cut out for that job.
  你十分適合那項工作。

註　亦常以「be cut out + to do something」的句型出現，例如：
- You're really cut out to be a teacher.
  你十分適合當老師。

工作 On the Job

❸ on duty　值班；執勤

on（正在……）+ **duty**（職務）= 正在值班、執勤

解說　on 是指「正在……；處於……中」，例如：on fire（失火）、on sale（特賣）、on strike（罷工）、on vacation（休假中）、on business（洽公；出差）；因此，on duty 是指「值班；執勤」。

例
- He fell asleep while on duty.
  他值班時睡著了。

反　off duty 不值班

註　可在片語中插入字以形容職務的形式，如：on night/guard/emergency duty（值夜班／執勤警戒／執行緊急任務）。

---

❹ take over　接管；接替

（可分開片語）

take（承擔）+ **over**（轉移）= 接管

解說　take over 是指接管、接替某工作、部門、公司等；在軍事上，則指「佔領」。

例
- My assistant can take over until we hire somebody.
  我的助理可以接替，直到我們請到人。

- The city has been taken over by the enemy soldiers.
  這座城市已被敵軍佔領。

Lesson 17

註 「take over + from/for + 人」是指「接替某人」，其後可加上「as + 職稱」或「on + 任務或責任」，例如：

- Ms. Huntley has taken over for Mr. Adams on payroll entry.
  杭特莉女士已接管亞當斯先生負責的薪資登入作業。
- Ms. Carter has taken over for Mr. Cage as Marketing Manager.
  卡特女士已接管凱吉先生行銷經理的職務。
- From next week, Kate will be taking over from Tiffany in the service department.
  從下禮拜開始，凱特將接替客服部的帝芬妮。

❺ let slide　丟著不管；怠忽職守

可分開片語

let（讓）＋ **slide**（滑落）＝ 任其滑落

解說　let slide 是形容處理事情就像「任由東西從手中滑落」一般，也就是「撒手不管」。

例
- Roxy didn't do her homework last night but the teacher let it slide.
  羅克絲昨天沒做功課，但老師卻不管。

144

工作 On the Job

❻ carry on　繼續

carry（帶著走）**+ on**（繼續）**=** 繼續進行

解說　carry on 除單獨使用外，主要以「carry on + with + 事物」、「carry on + V-ing」這兩種句型出現，表示「繼續進行某事物」。

例
- Professor Smith carried on with his research in secret.
  史密斯教授繼續秘密進行他的研究。

註　雖然「carry on + with + 事物」句型中的 with 有時可省略，但在此建議讀者還是加上比較不會出錯。

❼ set up　設立；裝設（機器等）

set（安置）**+ up**（起來）**=** 設立；裝設

解說　set up 的意思相當多，在此僅介紹其中兩種：

1.「設立；創設」公司、制度等
2.「架設；裝設」機器、帳篷等

例
- This is a great place to set up camp.
  這是個搭帳篷的好地方。

- The government set up an institute for education.
  政府建立了一所教育機構。

❽ stand for　代表；忍受

stand（站立）+ **for**（為了）= 為……站出來；為……一直站著

解說　stand for 有「代表」和「忍受」之意，兩者皆由「站立」所衍生。

例
- The color red stands for danger.
  紅色代表危險。
- You know I could never stand for this.
  你知道我絕對無法忍受這樣。

註　作「忍受」解時，常用於否定句及疑問句，**put up with** 為其相似詞。

---

❾ lay off　解雇；裁員　（可分開片語）

lay（放置）+ **off**（中斷地）= 置於中斷的狀態

解說　原指因為經濟不景氣等緣故而暫時解雇員工，將來景氣好時再回聘，但如今已無此意，常譯為「解雇；裁員」。

例
- I just heard that fifty people are going be laid off next month.
  我剛聽到下個月要裁掉五十名員工。

⑩ call it a day　結束當天的工作

call（叫）+ **it**（它）+ **a day**（一天）= 宣告一天工作結束

解說　這是工作場所常聽到的一個用語，意思是「結束當天的工作；下班了」。

例
- It's time to call it a day.
  下班時間到了。

聯　call it a night 結束當晚的工作

活用狄克生片語　　Lesson 17　複習測驗

一、選擇題（請選出一個最適當的選項）

1. Paul was sick and couldn't go to work, so he asked me to _____ him.
   (A) cover for　　(B) on duty of　　(C) take over　　(D) let slide

2. I'm very short, so I'm not _____ basketball.
   (A) on duty　　(B) cut out for　　(C) take over　　(D) account for

3. The doctor will be _____ at 6:00 p.m., so come at that time.
   (A) on duty　　(B) take over　　(C) carry on　　(D) cut out for

4. When my dad retires, I'll _____ the family company.
   (A) cut out for　　(B) take over　　(C) call it a day　　(D) lay off

二、翻譯填空

1. 我總是被期望在班上考第一，我父親不容許有更差的名次。
   I was always expected to be the best in my class; my father wouldn't _____ _____ anything less.

2. 我們家過去最糟的時刻是，當我父親被解雇。
   The worst time in our family's history was when my dad was _____ _____ from work.

3. 當我大學畢業，我要開設自己的公司。
   When I finish university, I want to _____ _____ my own company.

三、中翻英

1. 我沒做家庭作業，但老師這次卻不管。

2. 即使我做完家庭作業，我還繼續讀一整晚。

3. 今天工作就到此為止。

Lesson 18

狀況 Situations

One of my favorite things to do is babysit in my neighborhood. On the whole,[1] there's nothing to do but just be there with the kids. However, sooner or later, something is bound to[2] come up.

The one time my boyfriend came to study with me stands out.[3]

I got this great babysitting job thanks to[4] my mom's friend. Things were really looking up[5] for me. The house was a huge mansion and all in all[6] the kids were pretty well behaved.

As usual[7] I got there on time, and was looking up my boyfriend's number on my cell phone. Suddenly, he knocked on the door. It scared me a little and I turned around[8] fast and nearly smashed this expensive vase on a table. This was a really close call.[9] That was the last straw,[10] and from then on, I only babysit with the television for company.

Lesson 18

❶ on the whole　大體上；大致上

on（依據）**+ the whole**（整體）**=** 就整體而言

解說　on the whole 是指 all things considered（將所有事情都考慮進去）之後對整件事情的評價或看法，即「大體上；大致上」。

例
- On the whole, I think we made the right decision.
  大體上，我認為我們作了正確的決定。

似　all in all、by and large「大體而言；整個來說」

---

❷ be bound to　一定會

be bound（有義務的）**+ to**（不定詞）**=** 負有……的義務；一定會

解說　bound 是 bind 的過去分詞，在此其字義屬於較古老的用法指「有義務的」，而 be bound to 除指「負有……的義務」，常引申指「一定會」。

例
- If the project fails, our company is bound to lose the client.
  如果這個專案失敗，我們公司一定會失去這個客戶。

似　「be sure to + V.」（必定會）、「cannot fail to + V.」（一定會；絕對會）。

❸ stand out   顯著；突出

stand（豎立）+ **out**（突出地）= 突出地豎立著

解說 stand out 意思是「顯著；突出」，其後常會加上「from / among / above + 受詞」。

例
- Because he was so tall, Jason really stood out from the crowd.
  因為長得高，傑生在人群裡顯得很突出。

聯 stand out in a crowd 出眾

❹ thanks to   幸虧

thanks（感謝）+ **to**（對）= 要感謝……

解說 thanks to (someone / something) 並非指「要感謝某人或某物」，而是引申指某事之所以能成功或順利進展，是「多虧有……的緣故」或「托……的福」。

例
- Thanks to Bob, we were able to complete the project on schedule.
  多虧鮑伯，我們才能準時完成這個專案。

反 no thanks to 完全沒有幫助

❺ be looking up　逐漸好轉；有起色

be looking（逐漸朝……）**＋ up**（向上）**＝** 逐漸向上

解說　此處的 look 意思是「朝……；面對……」，而「事物 + be looking up」常用來形容事情、情況等「逐漸變好；有起色」。

例
- Finally, our financial situation is looking up.
  我們的財務狀況終於好轉。

聯　things are looking up (for + 人) 情況對（某人而言）逐漸好轉

註　亦可不使用進行式，例如：

- I hope our financial situation will start to look up in the new year.
  我希望我們的財務狀況在新的一年可以好轉。

---

❻ all in all　整體而言

all（全部）**＋ in**（在裡面）**＋ all**（全部）**＝** 將所有事情都考慮進去

解說　all in all 是指 all things considered（將所有事情都考慮進去）之後對整件事情的評價或看法，即「整體而言；總之」。

例
- All in all, I believe that life in the city is more convenient in every way.
  總之，我認為都市生活在各方面都比較方便。

似　on the whole、by and large「大致上；整體而言」

狀況 Situations

❼ as usual　通常；一如往常

as（如同）＋ **usual**（往常的）＝ 一如往常

解說　as usual 用來表示事情、情況等「一如往常」。

例
- I went to school that morning around 7:00 as usual.
  我那天早上和往常一樣七點上學。

似　「it is usual (for someone) + to V.」（某人）通常都是……

- It is usual for me to go to school around 7:00.
  我通常都是七點去上學。

❽ turn around　轉身；逆轉　可分開片語

turn（轉向）＋ **around**（調頭）＝ 轉身；逆轉

解說　turn around 原指「調頭轉向相反的方向」，除指「轉過身來」外，亦常用來形容事情、情況等「完全改觀開始好轉」，或「改變先前的意見、想法」。

例
- The police officer told the criminal to turn around slowly.
  警察叫罪犯慢慢轉過身來。
- We need to find a way to turn our company around.
  我們得設法讓我們公司的生意好起來。

Lesson 18

❾ close call　千鈞一髮

close（緊密的）＋ **call**（裁判的判決）＝ 裁判作出判決的瞬間

解說　源自運動競賽，指裁判作出判決的瞬間，高下立判；如今則引申用來形容「千鈞一髮；僥倖脫險」。

例
- We had a close call on the freeway when a large truck almost hit our car.
我們在高速公路上真是千鈞一髮，差點被一輛大卡車撞到。

同　close shave 千鈞一髮

---

❿ last straw　達到容忍極限

last（最後的）＋ **straw**（稻草）＝ 最後一根稻草

解說　源自西方諺語 the straw that broke the camel's back（壓垮駱駝的最後一根稻草），常簡稱 the last straw。我們都知道駱駝是很能負重的動物，如果不斷往駱駝背上加重物，總會達到駱駝負重的極限，這時那怕是再多加一根稻草，也會讓駱駝承受不住而倒地不起。如今，the last straw 常用來表示「達到容忍的極限」。

例
- When Danny stood me up for the third time, it was the last straw.
當丹尼第三次放我鴿子時，我實在忍無可忍。

似　be fed up with 受夠了

活用狄克生片語　Lesson 18 複習測驗

一、選擇題（請選出一個最適當的選項）

1. Some parts of the trip were good, others bad; _____, I liked it.
   (A) at best　　(B) at last　　(C) on the whole　(D) as usual

2. A tourist who stays in Hollywood long enough _____ see a movie star, eventually.
   (A) is bound to　(B) of course　(C) all in all　(D) as usual

3. We almost had a car accident; it was a _____ .
   (A) last straw　(B) close call　(C) first call　(D) last call

4. That's the _____. Don't say bad things about me again!
   (A) close call　(B) first call　(C) last call　(D) last straw

二、翻譯填空

1. 我們開錯方向了，所以我們必須調頭往回走。
   We were driving in the wrong direction, so we had to _____ _____ and go the other way.

2. 我弟弟通過考試要歸功於一位家教的協助。
   My brother passed the test _____ _____ some help from a private tutor.

3. 雖然我高中生活經驗既緊張又有趣，但整體而言，我必須說我學到很多。
   Although my high school experience was both interesting and stressful; all _____ _____, I'd have to say I learned a lot.

三、中翻英

1. 如果你想成功，就必須與眾不同。
   _____

2. 湯尼一如往常上課遲到。
   _____

3. 台灣現在的情況正在好轉。
   _____

解答請參閱第267頁

Notes

Lesson 19

程度 Extent

When I was in school, there was a rumor going around[1] that anyone who wanted to be in a movie just needed to show up at a certain studio and at least[2] get an audition.

I wanted to try. I was by no means[3] an actor; in fact, I had never acted at all.[4] My friend Trent, who was by far[5] better looking than I was, went with me.

In addition to[6] reading a couple of lines, we had to play a game of pool. I can play pool, more or less,[7] but I'm an average player at best.[8]

Trent and I did a scene together where we played a game of pool and got into an argument. The scene was great, but the camera had run out of[9] film after my second line. The director just let us play it out.

To sum up[10] my movie career, I'd say I'm no movie star, but I sure had fun!

Lesson 19

❶ go around 散播；足夠分配

go（行進）**+ around**（到處；繞一圈）**=** 散播；繞行一圈

解說　go around 可指疾病、消息等一個傳一個四處「散播」；也可以指食物、物品等「足夠分配」，可以一個接一個傳送給大家，繞一圈回來還有剩。

例
- Jake heard on the news that there was a deadly virus going around.
  傑克從新聞上得知有種致命的病毒正在散播。

- Jenny cooked so much that there was more than enough food to go around.
  珍妮煮了好多菜，絕對夠大家吃。

聯　be enough to go around 足夠分配

---

❷ at least 至少

at（以）**+ least**（最少）**=** 至少

解說　此處的 least 作名詞用，指「最少之數量、限度等」，at least 意思是「至少」，也可寫作 at the least。

例
- For international flights, you should arrive at least two hours early.
  搭國際航班至少應該提早兩個小時到達。

- At least you should buy me dinner first.
  起碼你得先請我吃晚飯。

程度 Extent

| 反 | at (the) most 至多 |
| 聯 | at the very least 至少至少也要……（這是強調用法，通常是指會比所說的數量多很多） |

❸ by no means　絕不；一點也不

by（藉由）＋ **no**（沒有任何）＋ **means**（方法）＝ 無論如何都不行

解說	by no means 用來表示堅決地否定，即「絕不；一點也不」。
例	• It is by no means certain that we'll finish the project by July. 這個專案現在根本無法確定會不會在七月完成。
同	not by any means 絕不；一點也不
反	by all means 一定；務必

❹ at all　一點也；到底

at（以）＋ **all**（所有）＝ 就各方面來看；在任何程度上

| 解說 | at all 作副詞用，若用於否定句意思是「一點也不」；若用於疑問句則指「到底；究竟」。 |
| 例 | • I'm not familiar with Taipei at all, so I'm not sure which bus to take.
我對台北一點也不熟，所以我不確定要搭哪一路公車。 |

159

Lesson 19

- Do you feel better at all?
  你到底有沒有覺得舒服一點？

---

❺ by far 遠高於；顯著地

by（相差）+ **far**（遠遠地）= 相差很遠

解說 by far 常用來加強比較級、最高級。

例
- This is by far the coolest web site I have ever used.
  這顯然是我用過最酷的網站。

---

❻ in addition to 除……之外

in addition（外加）+ **to**（到）= 除……之外

解說 in addition to 作介系詞用，表示「除……之外」，to 後面必須接名詞或 V-ing。

例
- In addition to turning in many assignments every day, we also have lots and lots of tests.
  每天除了要交很多作業外，我們還有考不完的試。

似 besides、aside from、apart from「除……之外」

程度 Extent

註　　in addition（況且；除……之外）為副詞片語。

- The lecture hall was overfilled; in addition, the first speaker had not shown up.
  這講堂太擠，此外，第一位演講者也還沒出現。

❼ more or less　或多或少；差不多

more（較多）+ **or**（或）+ **less**（較少）= 或多或少；差不多

解說　more or less 作副詞用，表示在程度上「或多或少」或與實際「差別不大」。

例
- Tony is more or less drunk.
  湯尼多少有點醉了。
- What he says is more or less true.
  他所說的差不多就是事實。

❽ at best　充其量；頂多

at（以）+ **best**（最好）= 就最好的方面而言

解說　用來表示所說的已是最佳情況，「充其量；頂多」也只能如此，不可能更好。

例
- She's an average student, at best.
  她頂多只是一個普通的學生。

Lesson 19

反　　at worst 最糟也不過是……

---

❾ run out of　用完

run（跑；流動）＋ **out of**（消失；用盡）＝ 跑光；流光

解說　run out of 表示「用光；用罄」，其中的 out of 本身即有「用盡」之意，例如：We're out of milk.（我們牛奶喝完了）。

例
- We've run out of milk; please buy some more.
  我們的牛奶喝完了，請再多買一些。

似　run short of 快要用完

---

❿ sum up　總計；作總結　〈可分開片語〉

sum（合計）＋ **up**（完全地）＝ 總計；作總結

解說　sum up 可指將所有數字、金額整個「作總計」，或抽象地指對演講、報告等「作總結；概括陳述」。

例
- Phil summed up his speech with a personal story.
  菲爾的演講以一個私人故事作總結。

活用狄克生片語　　Lesson 19 複習測驗

一、選擇題（請選出一個最適當的選項）

1. The flu is _____ school, so make sure you wash your hands frequently.
   (A) going over (B) getting out of (C) running out of (D) going around

2. I didn't play with the team the whole season; I thought I'd _____ play one game.
   (A) more or less (B) at least (C) look up on (D) by no means

3. We had to stay all day and practice, but it was _____ boring.
   (A) by far (B) all in all (C) by no means (D) at all

4. They wanted me to act, but I had no experience _____.
   (A) at most (B) at best (C) at least (D) at all

二、翻譯填空

1. 這本書第一部分還好，但第二部分顯然是最好的。
   The first part of the book was okay, but the second was _____ _____ the best.

2. 除了贏得寫作比賽外，我還贏了數學挑戰賽。
   _____ _____ _____ winning the writing contest, I won the math challenge.

3. 這老師是嚴格，但我多少有些同意她的教學方式。
   The teacher was strict, but I agree with her methods, _____ _____ _____.

三、中翻英

1. 雖然我是個很好的作家，但我頂多只是個普通的演講者。
   _____

2. 這家公司可能很快就把錢用光了。
   _____

3. 總之，我認為父母是一個人生命中最重要的親人。
   _____

解答請參閱第268頁

Notes

Lesson 20

反應 Reactions

Did you ever notice in school how the cool kids always seem to have their way?[1]

Those are the same kids who look down on[2] those of us who get good grades. They get carried away[3] with their own coolness and show off,[4] especially for their friends. They take it for granted[5] that everyone will play up to[6] them.

Well, I'm not going to put up with[7] it any more! I'm going to tell them how I feel about it, once and for all![8]

Don't worry, I won't get angry. I'll keep my head.[9]

You just better make believe[10] you don't know me in case they come after me!

Lesson 20

❶ have one's way　照某人的意思去做

have（擁有）＋ **one's**（某人的）＋ **way**（做法）＝ 照某人的意思去做

解說　have/get one's (own) way 是指「照某人的意思去做」，其中的 own 經常省略，亦可指「為所欲為；我行我素」。

例
- Don't let your children get their own way all the time.
  別老是讓你的孩子為所欲為。

---

❷ look down on　瞧不起；輕視

look（看）＋ **down**（向下）＋ **on**（在……上）＝ 向下看

解說　look down on 除指「向下俯瞰」外，常引申指「瞧不起；輕視」。

例
- Anne's grandmother looks down on poor people.
  安的祖母瞧不起窮人。

同　look down one's nose at 瞧不起；輕視

反　look up to 尊敬

反應 Reactions

❸ get carried away　忘情於；不能自己

get（達到……狀態）＋ **carried**（被帶走）＋ **away**（離開）＝ 不能自己

解說　be/get carried away 常用來形容一個人過於投入、熱衷某事物，好像整個人的神智、心思被帶走似的，而「不能自己」。

例
- The audience got carried away by the singer's songs.
  這位歌手的歌聲讓聽眾渾然忘我。

註　get carried away 亦可指「做得太過火」（通常指衝動行事，往往做得太過而不自知）

- Tommy got carried away with his pranks.
  湯米的玩笑開得太過分了。

---

❹ show off　賣弄；炫耀　（可分開片語）

show（展示）＋ **off**（完全地）＝ 賣弄；炫耀

解說　show off 除可單獨使用，亦可接受詞以表示「賣弄、炫耀……」。

例
- John was always showing off, trying to impress the girls.
  約翰老是喜歡炫耀，以博取女孩子的青睞。

- Susan loves showing off her slim figure.
  蘇珊老愛炫耀她苗條的身材。

Lesson 20

❺ take for granted　視為理所當然

take for（把……當作）+ **granted**（被許可的）=把……視為被許可的

解說　「take（人／事物）for granted 是指「將……視作理所當然的」或「（因視作當然而）對……不予重視」。

例
- I take it for granted that you understand this project's importance to the company.
  我以為你應該知道這項方案對公司有多重要。

---

❻ play up to　討好

play（表演）+ **up**（有勁地）+ **to**（向）=向……賣力表演

解說　up 在此是指「有勁地」，類似的用法有：speak up（大聲說）、work up（刺激；煽動）等。讀者可想想，play up to「討好」是不是就像賣力為某人表演一樣。

例
- It is no use playing up to our math teacher for better grades.
  為了得到更好的成績而巴結我們數學老師是沒有用的。

似　flatter、butter up「奉承；討好」

反應 Reactions

❼ put up with　忍受

put up（撐著）**+ with**（與）**=** 撐著不爆發

解說　put up with 經常指「忍受；容忍」某人、事、物而沒有怨言。

例
- I don't know how much longer I can put up with the bad situation.
  我不知道我對這種惡劣的狀況還能忍多久。

❽ once and for all　僅此一次；斷然地

once（一次）**+ and**（而且）**+ for all**（永遠）**=** 只此一次永遠不再

解說　once and for all 是由 one time and for all time 衍生而來，指「只此一次，永遠不會再有下次」，即「一勞永逸地；斷然地」之意。

例
- We need to get this problem sorted out once and for all.
  我們必須徹底一次解決這個問題。

❾ keep one's head　保持冷靜

keep（保持）**+ one's**（某人的）**+ head**（理性）**=** 保持理性

解說　此處的 head 是指「頭腦；理性」，因此 keep one's head 的意思是「保持冷靜」。

例 • Please keep your head and tell me what happened.
請你保持冷靜,告訴我發生什麼事了。

同 stay calm、keep one's shirt on「保持冷靜」

❿ make believe 假裝

make（使）+ believe（相信）= 使（自己）信以為真

解說 make believe 原指「相信自己的幻覺、錯覺」,常用來表示「幻想、假裝……是真的」,其後常接 that 子句。

例 • Sometimes children make believe they have invisible friends.
小孩子有時候會幻想自己有隱形的朋友。

活用狄克生片語 Lesson 20 複習測驗

一、選擇題（請選出一個最適當的選項）

1. You can't _____ all the time; you need to share with others.
   (A) have your way (B) put up with (C) keep your head (D) look down on

2. She thinks she's better, so she _____ other people.
   (A) puts up to (B) gets away with (C) looks up on (D) looks down on

3. I'm sorry I couldn't stop talking; I guess I _____.
   (A) kept my head (B) put up with (C) got carried away (D) looked down on

4. Look at how she always answers the teacher's questions; she's _____.
   (A) showing off (B) playing up to (C) looking down on (D) putting up with

二、翻譯填空

1. 你父母給你錢幫助你，可不要將之視為理所當然。
   Your parents give you money to help you, but don't _____ _____ _____ _____.

2. 所有員工都在討好大老闆真讓我想吐。
   It makes me sick how all the employees _____ _____ _____ the big boss.

3. 好的父母不會容忍孩子的錯誤不管，而會予以糾正。
   A good parent doesn't _____ _____ _____ their children's mistakes, they correct them.

三、中翻英

1. 我要確定我們一勞永逸地解決這個問題。
   _____

2. 當你遇到危險狀況時，最好保持冷靜。
   _____

3. 假裝問題不存在，並不會讓問題消失遠離。
   _____

Notes

Lesson 21

支持 Support

I'm the kind of person who people seem to come to when they need something. I try to live up to[1] the image that my friends have of me that there is nothing out of the question.[2] However, I do draw the line[3] at some things.

When someone asks me for a favor, by all means,[4] I try not to turn down[5] anyone's request. Keep your fingers crossed[6] that I never have to! I may not always see eye to eye[7] with what they need from me, but I take them at their word[8] that it's important and they need my help. If I don't do it, who's going to stand up for[9] them?

It doesn't make me a hero, so don't give me a big hand[10] or a medal. It just makes me someone who cares and wants to help.

Lesson 21

❶ live up to   遵守；達到

live（生活）+ **up to**（達到）= 在生活中實踐、達到

解說　「live up to + 事物」用來表示「遵行（某事物）；達到（期待或標準）」。

例
- Rick found it hard trying to live up to his father's expectations.
  瑞克覺得很難達到他父親的期望。

---

❷ out of the question   不可能；門都沒有

out of（在……之外）+ **the question**（這問題）= 不納入此問題

解說　out of the question 字面意思是「不去談論某事」或「將某事完全排除在外」，常用來表示「不可能；門都沒有」。

例
- Our teacher said canceling the test was out of the question.
  我們老師說考試不可能取消。

比　beyond question 無庸置疑

支持 Support

❸ draw the line at　　拒絕；到此為止

draw（畫）＋ **the line**（一條線）＋ **at**（對……）＝ 對……畫出界線

解説　「draw the line at + 事物」常引申指「拒絕某事物」或「某事物只到此為止」。

例
- I drew the line at her request.
  我拒絕了她的請求。

比　draw the line (between something) 使……有區別
- Where do you draw the line between friendship and flirtation?
  你對友誼和調情之間的界限為何？

---

❹ by all means　　無論如何；務必

by（藉由；用）＋ **all**（所有的）＋ **means**（方法）＝ 用盡所有可能的方法

解説　表示就算用盡所有可能的方法，「無論如何」、「務必」達成某事。此外，也常用來允許別人做某事，或答應別人的請求。

例
- I want you to bring him here by all means.
  我要你務必他來這裡。
- "May I borrow your pen?" "By all means."
  「可以借你的筆嗎？」「當然可以。」

反　by no means 絕不；一點也不

❺ turn down　拒絕；減低　可分開片語

turn（轉變）＋ **down**（向下）＝ 轉變向下

解說　turn down 用來表示「拒絕」或將聲音「關小」、亮度「調暗」、速度「減慢」。

例
- Rachel turned down Paul's offer to help.
  瑞秋拒絕保羅的幫忙。
- Could you turn down the radio?
  麻煩你把收音機關小聲一點好嗎？

似1　refuse、reject「拒絕」

似2　turn up 調大聲；轉強

---

❻ keep one's fingers crossed　祈求

keep（保持）＋ **one's fingers**（某人的手指）＋ **crossed**（交叉）
＝ 保持手指交叉

解說　從前人們相信：食指和中指交叉的手勢，與十字架一樣具有驅魔的力量，因此 keep one's fingers crossed 便表示「祈求好運降臨」。

例
- Let's keep our fingers crossed that you will get the promotion.
  讓我們祈求你會被升職。

支持 Support

註　cross one's fingers 除可表示「祈求好運降臨」外，亦有「撒謊」的意思。這是因為小孩子在撒謊時，常會在背後將食指和中指交叉，認為這樣就不算說謊！

❼ see eye to eye　　意見一致

see（看見）＋ **eye to eye**（大家的眼睛）＝ 大家都會看見

解說　源自聖經《以賽亞書》，原指「大家都會看見」，引申指「意見一致」，常用於否定句。

例
- Helen and Tim don't see eye to eye on politics.
  海倫和提姆的政治觀點不同。

註　「see eye to eye + on 事物」、「see eye to eye + with 人」這兩個句型分別指「對事物」、「與某人」的意見一致。

❽ take at one's word　　相信某人說的話

take（接受）＋ **at**（以；就）＋ **one's word**（某人的話）＝ 相信某人說的話

解說　源自聖經《列王記上》，表示「相信某人說的話」，常以「take + 人 + at one's word」句型出現。

例
- I don't know whether to take him at his word or not.
  我不知道到底要不要相信他的話。

| 同 | take someone's word for it 相信某人說的話

• He said he would help me out and I took his word for it.
他說會幫我，我就相信了他的話。

---

❾ stand up for　支持；維護

stand（站立）+ **up**（起來）+ **for**（為了）= 為了……站出來

| 解說 | stand up for 意思是「捍衛（某事）；支持（某人）；維護（某事物）」，翻譯時需視上下文而定。

| 例 | • Frank always stands up for his younger brother against bullies.
法蘭克總是為他弟弟挺身而出，對付欺負他的人。

| 比 | stand up to 挺身對抗某人或物

• Susan finally found the courage to stand up to her older sister.
蘇珊終於鼓起勇氣對抗她姊姊。

---

❿ give (someone) a big hand　為……掌聲鼓勵

give someone（給某人）+ **a big hand**（熱烈掌聲）= 為……掌聲鼓勵

| 解說 | 此處的 hand 是「拍手；鼓掌」，big 是形容掌聲「熱烈」，常以「give + 人 + a big hand」句型表示「為……掌聲鼓勵」。

| 例 | • Let's give him a big hand.
让我們為他掌聲鼓勵。

| 似 | give it up for、applaud for「為……掌聲鼓勵」

| 聯 | get a big hand 獲得掌聲

| 比 | give (someone) a hand 常用來表示「幫忙（某人）」，亦可表示「為（某人）鼓掌」。

活用狄克生片語　Lesson 21 複習測驗

一、選擇題（請選出一個最適當的選項）

1. They said he was a great actor, but his performance didn't _____ his reputation.
   (A) live up to　　(B) draw up to　　(C) stand up for　　(D) call for

2. You have a test tomorrow, so staying out late is _____.
   (A) beyond question　　　　(B) out of the question
   (C) by all means　　　　　(D) by no means

3. I have been nice so far, but now I have to _____.
   (A) give a big hand　　(B) draw the line　　(C) turn down　　(D) stand up for

4. You're my guest, so _____ help yourself to some finger sandwiches.
   (A) stand up for　　(B) live up to　　(C) by no means　　(D) by all means

二、翻譯填空

1. 在一個浪漫的晚餐後我向她求婚，但她拒絕了我。
   I asked her to marry me after a romantic dinner, but she _____ _____ _____.

2. 我知道你想獲得這份工作，所以我會為你祈禱。
   I know you want to get this job, so I'll _____ _____ fingers _____ for you.

3. 對此我和你看法不同，因為我認為你的資料不正確。
   I don't _____ _____ _____ _____ with you on this because I think your data is incorrect.

三、中翻英

1. 如果你相信某事物，就應該擁護它。
   _____

2. 這聽起來雖然負面，但我不認為你該聽信別人的話。
   _____

3. 這是我第一次公開表演，觀眾給我熱烈掌聲。
   _____

Lesson 22

關係 Relationships

When you grow up in the same neighborhood, like Brian and I did, you develop a special give and take[1] relationship. We got along with[2] each other like brother and sister. When we got older, we both changed. He came across[3] more as a boyfriend than brother.

I never expected I would fall for[4] him, but it happened. I never let on[5] how deeply I loved him. When we started high school we went steady. He used to take care of[6] me just like I imagined a boyfriend should. When we would argue, he would always apologize and make up with[7] me.

In our senior year his family moved away and we had to break off,[8] but I still hear from[9] him every month. I know one of these days he's going to stop fooling around[10] and come back to me.

Lesson 22

❶ give and take　相互忍讓；彼此妥協

give（給與）＋ **and**（和）＋ **take**（接受）＝ 施與受

解說　give and take 雖然是動詞形式，但主要卻作名詞用，意思是「彼此為對方多付出一點」，即「相互忍讓；彼此妥協」之意。

例
- In any relationship there has to be some give and take.
  在任何情感關係中，都需要相互忍讓。

註　亦可寫作 give-and-take。

---

❷ get along with　相處融洽

get（達到）＋ **along**（一起）＋ **with**（和）＝ 與……相處在一起

解說　get along with 後面若不加受詞，with 便可省略，意思是「相處融洽」。

例
- I was surprised that Kathy got along with Jason so well.
  我很訝異凱西竟然和傑生相處得這麼好。
- Kathy and Jason don't get along.
  凱西和傑生相處不來。

同　get on with 相處融洽

比　get along without 沒有……也能處理、進行

聯　I'd better be getting along 我看我得走了

關係 Relationships

❸ come across　不期而遇；給予印象

come（來）**+ across**（穿越）**=** 與……交會

解說　come across 常指「不期而遇」，但也可以抽象地表示「在腦海裡產生」，即「給人……的印象」。

例
- You'll never guess who I came across at the party!
  你絕對猜不到我在派對上遇見了誰！
- Jenny came across well to my mother.
  珍妮留給我媽媽很好的印象。

註1　若表示「給予印象」，常會像課文中一樣用「come across as + 呈現的印象」來表示。

註2　「come across + with 事物」則指「提供所需之事物或訊息」。

---

❹ fall for　迷戀；被騙

fall（落下）**+ for**（為了）**=** 為……而傾心；上鉤

解說　源自魚看到魚餌時的動作，引申指「迷戀；被騙」。表「迷戀」要用「fall for + 人」；表「被騙」要用「fall for + 事物」。

例
- Tony is the last man she'd ever fall for.
  湯尼是她最不可能愛上的男人。
- She falls for his lies again and again.
  她一再地被他的謊言所欺騙。

Lesson 22

❺ let on　洩露；透露

> **let**（讓）＋ **on**（開著）＝ 讓秘密流露出來

解說　let on 是指「透露」消息、秘密等，其後經常接子句，例如：「let on + that/who/how/why 子句」。若要接名詞或片語，則要用「let on + about 事物（to 人）」句型表示。

例
- Don't let on to Jenny that I told you about the party.
  別讓珍妮知道，我跟你說過派對的事。
- Don't let on about the party to Jenny. It's a surprise party for her!
  別讓珍妮知道派對的事，那是為她舉辦的驚喜派對！

似　let out 說出；透露（其後可接名詞、片語或子句）

---

❻ take care of　照顧；處理

> **take**（承擔）＋ **care**（照顧）＋ **of**（對……的）＝ 承擔對……的照顧

解說　「take care of + 人／事物」是表示「照顧（人）；處理（事物）」。

例
- I'll be able to take care of myself.
  我可以自己照顧自己。
- I'll take care of it. Don't worry.
  這我會處理，別擔心。

關係 Relationships

比　take care 小心；注意；保重
　　• Please take care when you're driving on ice.
　　　當你開車在結冰的路上時可要小心。

❼ make up with　重修舊好

make（製作）+ **up**（完成）+ **with**（和）= 將彼此間的……補起來

解說　此處的 make up 是指將彼此的誤解、間隙等「補起來」，make up with 意思是「重修舊好；復合」。

例　• Tony was planning to make up with his ex-girlfriend.
　　　湯尼打算和他前女友復合。

❽ break off　斷絕；分手

可分開片語

break（斷裂）+ **off**（切斷）= 斷絕；終止

解說　break off 常指「斷絕」relations（關係）、「終止」contract（合約）、engagement（婚約）等。

例　• Chad broke off diplomatic relations with Taiwan.
　　　查德與台灣斷交。

註　若指「分手」則常用「break it off + with 人」句型來表示。

似　break up（with 人）分手

Lesson 22

❾ hear from　得到某人的音訊

hear（聽到）＋ **from**（來自）＝ 聽到某人所說的話

解說　hear from 有兩種意思：一為「聽某人談論某事」，另一為「得到某人的音訊、來信或來電等」。

例
- Mary moved to Canada last year, and I haven't heard from her since.
  瑪麗去年搬到加拿大，從此再也沒有她的音訊。
- And next, I'd like to hear from Jenny.
  接下來，我想聽珍妮說一下。

比　hear of 聽到；聽說

---

❿ fool around　鬼混；胡鬧

fool（做傻事）＋ **around**（到處）＝ 鬼混

解說　fool around 是指閒蕩、不做正經事、虛擲光陰，即「鬼混；胡鬧」之意，但若指男女之間，則有「胡搞」之意。

例
- Stop fooling around in class!
  上課時別胡鬧！

似　goof/horse around 鬼混；胡鬧

活用狄克生片語　Lesson 22 複習測驗

一、選擇題（請選出一個最適當的選項）

1. Try not to be so selfish; you need to learn to _____.
   (A) get along　　(B) give and take　(C) let on　　　　(D) make up

2. I don't really _____ my co-workers because we see things differently.
   (A) stand up for　(B) break off with　(C) get along with　　(D) come across as

3. He may be humorous, but he _____ being very serious.
   (A) falls for　　(B) takes care of　(C) comes across　　(D) comes across as

4. When I saw how beautiful and smart she was, I immediately _____ her.
   (A) fell for　　(B) broke off with　(C) heard from　　(D) let go of

二、翻譯填空

1. 我寧願將我的感情隱藏起來，也不透露我有多喜歡他。
   I'd prefer to keep my feelings secret and not _____ _____ how much I like him.

2. 當父母到了某個年紀，照顧他們是很重要的。
   It's important to _____ _____ _____ your parents when they reach a certain age.

3. 爭吵過後，我們重新和好並決定不再相互吼對方。
   After the argument, we _____ _____ and decided not to yell at each other anymore.

三、中翻英

1. 為了出國唸書，我必須和男朋友分手。

   _____

2. 我離開加拿大後，從未收到蘇珊的訊息。

   _____

3. 別胡鬧了！是該認真點了。

   _____

解答請參閱第270頁

Notes

Lesson 23

安排 Making Arrangements

My friends and I really enjoy camping. When we set out to[1] plan a camping trip, we think over[2] where we'd like to go and what type of terrain we prefer for that trip.

We take into account[3] the time of year, what activities we want to do, and the distance we'd have to travel. We don't rule out[4] anywhere, because if we plan in advance,[5] we can get reservations almost anyplace we feel like[6] going.

Jake is the leader of our group and he's really on the ball.[7] We'll tell him what we have in mind,[8] and in case[9] he doesn't know the place, he knows someone who does.

It figures[10] he always manages to get us the choice spots at the campground.

Lesson 23

❶ set out to 開始做;打算

set（朝）+ **out**（向外）+ **to**（不定詞）= 開始去做

解說 set out 有「出發」之意,而「set out to + V.」則指「開始進行以期能達成某事」。

例
- He set out to realize his dreams by working hard.
  他開始努力打拼以實現夢想。

比 set out for 出發前往

❷ think over 仔細考慮   可分開片語

think（思考）+ **over**（從頭到尾）= 仔細考慮

解說 此處的 over 是指「從頭到尾;全部」,類似用法有:read over（全部看過、讀過）、go over（仔細討論、檢查）,而 think over 則指「仔細考慮」。

例
- Why don't you think it over and give me a reply later?
  你何不仔細想想,稍後再給我答覆?

比 think through / out 徹底考慮;想透

安排 Making Arrangements

❸ take into account　加以考慮

take（取得）+ **into**（進入）+ **account**（計算）= 把……計算在內

解說　字面意思是「把……納入計算」，引申指「對……加以考慮」。

例
- Jenny doesn't eat meat, so take that into account when you plan dinner.
  珍妮不吃肉，你準備晚餐時要考量這一點。

同　take account of、take into consideration「加以考慮」

反　take no account of、leave out of account「完全不考慮」

❹ rule out　排除；不予考慮　　（可分開片語）

rule（裁決）+ **out**（在外）= 排除在外

解說　字面意思是「決定將……排除在外」，因而衍生出「排除……的可能性」之含意。

例
- Ms. Whitman has been ruled out as a candidate to succeed Mr. Brown.
  惠特曼小姐已被排除成為布朗先生的接替人選。

聯　「rule + 人 + out of + 競賽」句型常用來表示「某人因……而無法參賽」。

Lesson 23

❺ in advance 事先；預先

in（在）+ **advance**（前進）= 在前面；事先

解說 advance 原指「前進；進展」，in advance 則指「事先；預先」，作副詞用。

例
- We can do most of the preparation in advance.
  大多數的準備工作我們可以事先做。

比 in advance of 作介系詞用，指「在……之前；比……進步」。

- Please call to reconfirm your reservation 72 hours in advance of your flight.
  請在起飛前七十二小時再次確認預定的機位。

---

❻ feel like 想要……

feel（感覺）+ **like**（想要；像）= 覺得想要；覺得好像

解說 此處的 like 為介系詞，一般作「像……」解，因此，feel like 也有「覺得好像」之意，但在此意思則為「想要」。

例
- What do you feel like eating?
  你想吃什麼？

- Do you really feel like you learned a lot?
  你真的覺得有學到很多嗎？

註 常以「feel like + 名詞／動名詞」句型出現。

安排 Making Arrangements

❼ on the ball　機警；能幹

on（在……上）**+ the ball**（球）**=** 注視著球

解說　原指棒球的打擊者，必須全神貫注投手投出來的球。如今則引申指「機警；能幹」。

例
- They said I didn't look like I was on the ball.
  他們說我看起來不是很機警。

聯　have a lot on the ball 聰明機伶；身手不凡

❽ have in mind　想著；打算

have（有）**+ in**（在）**+ mind**（心）**=** 在心裡想著

解說　常以「have + 事物 + in mind」的形式出現，意思是「心中有某種想法」，即「想著；打算；考量」之意。

例
- What kind of new hairstyle did you have in mind?
  你想要剪什麼樣的新髮型？

比1　「have + 事物 + on one's mind」是指「擔心或惦記某事物」。

比2　out of mind 是指「發瘋的；心神錯亂的」

Lesson 23

❾ in case 以防萬一；要是……的話

in（在）+ **case**（事件）= 在……情況下

解說 in case 作連接詞時，常以「in case + 子句」表示「以防萬一；要是……的話」；若作副詞時，則常會在前面加上 just 以緩和語氣。

例
- We should take an umbrella in case it rains.
  我們應該帶把傘，以防萬一下雨。
- We should take an umbrella, just in case.
  我們應該帶把傘，以防萬一。

比 「in case of + 名詞」表示「要是遇到……情況」，常用來告訴別人遇到某種狀況時，應該如何因應或處理。

- In case of fire, do not use the elevators.
  火災發生時，切勿搭乘電梯。

❿ it figures 似乎有理；果不其然

it（它）+ **figures**（計算）= 算出

解說 原指「將數字計算出來」，如今則用來比喻「似乎有理；果不其然」。常以「it figures + that 子句」出現，亦可單獨使用。

例
- It figures that we would have a big test on the last day of school.
  上課最後一天我們應該會有一場大考。

- "I'm too tired to help with your homework." "It figures!"
「我太累了不能幫你做功課。」「我早就料到了。」

|同| that figures 似乎有理；果不其然

活用狄克生片語　Lesson 23 複習測驗

一、選擇題（請選出一個最適當的選項）

1. When I _____ accomplish something, I try to do it perfectly.
   (A) rule out to　(B) set out to　(C) get out to　(D) feel like

2. Before you do anything, you should _____ your plans carefully.
   (A) set out　(B) according to　(C) think over　(D) rule out

3. We wanted to play baseball, but we didn't _____ it would rain that day.
   (A) set out　(B) in case　(C) in advance　(D) take into account

4. When you ask a person a favor, don't _____ that they may say no.
   (A) set out to　(B) rule out　(C) on the ball　(D) in case

二、翻譯填空

1. 不管你打算在人生中做什麼，記住愛拼才會贏。
   Whatever you _____ _____ _____ to do in your life, remember that you can accomplish it with hard work.

2. 我不想試著去改變他的心意，所以就由他去吧。
   I didn't _____ _____ trying to change his mind, so I left him alone.

3. 我很早就花許多時間學英文，以防萬一有一天會用得上這項技能。
   I put a lot of time into English studies early on, just _____ _____ one day I would need that skill.

三、中翻英

1. 要在這間旅館預約，你必須一個月前事先打電話。

2. 經理立刻處理這個問題，她實在很機警。

3. 我沒有花時間準備考試，果不其然我並沒考好。

解答請參閱第271頁

Lesson 24

動作 Movement

Track 24

It had been many years since I'd ridden a horse, yet Dale insisted I go riding with him. I wanted to be able to keep up with[1] him on the trail because I know he likes to make good time.[2] I drove to the country to rent a horse to make a sort of dry run.[3]

The first horse I tried wouldn't pick up[4] its feet—or rather hooves. The second one I chose was more spirited, so I took hold of[5] the reins, but all he did was trot back and forth[6] from the gate to the paddock.*

The wrangler* brought out a third horse. "I hope he doesn't turn on[7] you!" he said "We call him 'Devil'." I told the cowboy to stick around[8] and watch a real rider! Devil didn't hold still[9] for long! In a minute I was flying through the air. I landed with a thud then rose to my feet[10] in a daze. "Devil's got spirit!" I said.

* paddock [ˈpædək] n.（賽馬場的）草地圍場
* wrangler [ˈræŋglɚ] n. 牧馬者；牛仔

Lesson 24

❶ keep up with　趕上；並駕齊驅

keep（保持）＋ **up**（完全）＋ **with**（與……一起）＝ 與……維持同一速度

解說　「keep up with + 人」是指「與某人並駕齊驅；趕上某人」，可指實際的速度，也可以抽象地表示在程度、能力上「趕上某人」。

例
- Tony could not keep up with the rest of the class.
  湯尼無法跟上班上其他同學。

❷ make good time　快速前進

make（達到）＋ **good**（好的）＋ **time**（時間）＝ 用很短的時間達到

解說　此處的 good time 是指「很短的時間」，並非「美好的時光」，而 make good time 則是「快速前進」之意。

例
- Once we got on the freeway, we made good time.
  我們一上到高速公路，就開得很快。

❸ dry run　排練；預演

dry（投彈模擬）＋ **run**（演練）＝ 投彈模擬演練

解說　源自軍事術語，原指「投彈模擬演練」，之所以用 dry 這個字，是將炸彈比作雨水，天沒下雨地上是乾的，而「投彈模擬」也是同樣的狀況，並不會投真的炸彈。

動作 Movement

如今，dry run 常引申指各種事物的「排練；預演」。

例
- The wedding rehearsal was a dry run for the ceremony the next day.
  這次婚禮彩排是為隔天的典禮預作演練。

---

❹ pick up　拾起；購買；搭載 〈可分開片語〉

pick（選取）＋ up（起來）＝ 拾起；取得

解說　pick up 除指「拾起；取得」外，還有很多意思，以下列舉其他一些常見的用法：

1. 「拾起；拿起」
   - Let me help you pick up your books.
     我來幫你把書撿起來。

2. 「取得（某物）；接送（某人）」
   - Can you pick up a pizza for me on your way home from work?
     你下班回家時可以順便幫我買個披薩嗎？

3. 「（非專程或刻意）學會；學到」
   - I hope to pick up some Spanish during my trip to Spain.
     我希望去西班牙旅遊時，可以順便學到一些西班牙語。

4. 「（收音機或麥克風等儀器）接收訊號」
   - Sorry. My radio can't pick up that station.
     抱歉，我的收音機無法收聽到那個電台。

5. 「接續；再開始（中斷過的活動、事件、情節等）」
   - I'd like to pick up where we left off at the last meeting.
     我想接續我們上次會議的討論。

❺ take hold of　握住;抓住

take（抓住）＋ **hold**（把握）＋ **of**（動作的對象）＝ 握住;抓住

[解說] take hold of 是指「去抓住某物」。

[例]
- The young boy took hold of his mother's arm after he heard the loud sound.
  小男孩聽到這巨大的聲響後,便緊抓著媽媽的手臂。

❻ back and forth　來回地;前後地

back（返回;向後）＋ **and**（又）＋ **forth**（向前）＝ 來回地;前後地

[解說] back and forth 是指在兩地之間「往返地;來回地」。

[例]
- The waiter walks back and forth from the kitchen to the dining room all evening.
  這名服務生整晚在廚房和餐室之間來回穿梭。

[同] to and fro、backward(s) and forward(s)「來回地」

❼ turn on　與……敵對;打開

turn（轉動）＋ **on**（對著;開著）＝ 與……敵對;轉開（電器、設備）

動作 Movement

| 解説 | 「turn on + 人」是指「與某人敵對」，若將「人」置於片語中間，則意思完全不同；「turn on + 電器、設備」則指「打開」電器、設備等。

| 例 | • Don't get John angry, he'll turn on you in a minute.
別惹約翰生氣，他會立刻跟你翻臉。

• Let's turn on the radio for news.
打開收音機來聽新聞吧。

| 比 | 「turn + 人 + on」是表示「使興奮；陶醉」、「使產生興趣；愛好」、「激起性慾」等，因此 turn on you（與你作對）和 turn you on（引起你的興趣或性慾）兩者可是有天壤之別。

• My brother was the first to turn me on to jazz music.
我哥哥是第一個讓我對爵士樂產生興趣的人。

| 反 | turn off 關掉；使不感興趣

---

❽ stick around　待在這裡等

stick（待著）＋ around（在附近）＝ 在附近等待

| 解説 | stick 一般作「固定不動」解，在此意思相當於 stay「待著」，而 stick around 的意思是「待在這裡等」，常用於事情比預期還要久，因此必須繼續「耐心等候」。

| 例 | • Do you want to stick around for a while?
你要不要待在這裡再等一會兒？

201

Lesson 24

❾ hold still　保持靜止　_{可分開片語}

hold（保持）＋ **still**（靜止的）＝ 保持靜止

解說　此處的 still（靜止的）雖為形容詞，亦可將之視為副詞，類似用法有 stand still（站著不動）、sit still（坐著不動）等，而 hold still 則指「保持靜止不動」。

例
- Hold still while I get this chewing gum out of your hair.
  你不要動，我幫你把頭髮上的口香糖弄下來。

---

❿ rise to one's feet　站起來

rise（起身）＋ **to**（向）＋ **one's feet**（某人雙腳）＝ 站起來

解說　rise to one's feet 是指從原本躺著或坐著等姿勢而「起身」。

例
- He rose to his feet and ran outside.
  他站起來往外跑。

同　get to one's feet、get on one's feet「站起來」

比　back on one's feet（從失敗、挫折中）重新站起來；（從疾病中）康復

- The company is back on its feet after suffering several financial losses.
  該公司歷經幾次財務虧損後又重新站起來。

活用狄克生片語　Lesson 24 複習測驗

一、選擇題（請選出一個最適當的選項）

1. You're walking too fast and I can't _____ you.
   (A) take hold of (B) stick around (C) keep up with (D) turn on

2. If we catch all the green lights, we'll _____ .
   (A) keep up with (B) turn on (C) rise to our feet (D) make good time

3. Before we actually try to use this, let's have a _____ and see if it works.
   (A) lost cause (B) dry run (C) back and forth (D) steal

4. The horse would not _____ its hooves and just stood still.
   (A) pick up (B) take hold of (C) kick around (D) turn on

二、翻譯填空

1. 我想最好還是待在這裡，確定沒人在這場意外中受傷。
   I thought it was better to _____ _____ and make sure that no one was injured in the accident.

2. 當這位歌劇女伶結束表演後觀眾都站了起來。
   The crowd _____ _____ _____ _____ when the opera singer finished her performance.

3. 如果野狗覺得受到威脅，便會與你敵對。
   Wild dogs will _____ _____ you if they feel threatened.

三、中翻英

1. 比賽前，我抓住方向盤（wheel），準備開跑。
   _____

2. 當醫生要給我打針時，我無法保持靜止不動。
   _____

3. 這些狼並未攻擊，他們只是來回踱步（pace），注視著我們。
   _____

Notes

Lesson 25

阻礙 Obstacles

Track 25

I'm a civil engineer. After I graduated from university, I went back to my hometown to make life easier for people there.

My hometown is a small place. The transportation system there was very inconvenient. Many of the railways, traffic lights, and street signals were out of order.[1] I wanted to get rid of[2] them and change the system. It prevented people from[3] going to work and coming home on time. People would be able to spend more time with their families but for[4] the town planning.

I went over[5] all my new plans with the town officials. They liked them. But change is never easy, and when we began work, things went wrong.[6] Every time I went to check up on[7] the progress, someone working on construction always interfered with[8] things. Of course, the construction workers thought I was in their way,[9] too. We couldn't agree on things.

However, in the end I learned that it is best not to make waves[10] and just talk to people. It was hard, but now my town is one of the safest and most convenient in the country.

Lesson 25

❶ out of order   雜亂無章；故障

out of（失去） + **order**（順序） = 雜亂無章；故障

解說 out of order 有兩層意思，一是字面意思「雜亂無章」，另一個意思則是指公用物品失去原有應有的運作機制，即「故障」之意。

例
- Be careful not to get the books out of order.
  小心別把書的順序給弄亂了。

- The elevators are out of order, so we'll have to take the stairs.
  電梯故障了，我們只好走樓梯。

比 一般來說，私人物品「壞了」要用 broken，而公用物品壞了則要用 out of order。（但電話屬於公用物品的範圍，由於只要有電話號碼便可與之聯絡，因此即使是私人電話壞了也要用 My phone is out of order.）

---

❷ get rid of 去除；擺脫

get（使） + **rid**（去除的） + **of**（動作的對象） = 去除；擺脫

解說 rid 在此為過去分詞作形容詞用，指「被從……去除的」，而 get rid of 則表示「去除；擺脫」討厭的人、事、物。

例
- The New Year is a new beginning and a good time to get rid of bad habits.
  新年是個新的開始，也是甩掉壞習慣的好時機。

阻礙 Obstacles

❸ prevent from　阻礙；防止

prevent（阻礙）＋ **from**（分離；從……）＝ 阻礙；防止

解說　prevent 本身便有「阻礙；防止」之意，因此介系詞 from 經常可省略，常以「prevent（人／事物）(from) + V-ing」句型出現。

例
- His arm injury may prevent him from playing in tomorrow's game.
他手臂受傷可能明天無法出賽。

❹ but for　若非

but（如果不……）＋ **for**（因為）＝ 如果不是因為……

解說　but for 作介系詞用，為假設語氣用法，意思相當於 were it not for（要不是因為）。

例
- But for all these interruptions, our meeting would have finished earlier.
要不是被打斷這麼多次，我們的會議早就開完了。

註　but for 若非假設語氣用法，意思則是「但是對於……」。

Lesson 25

❺ go over   仔細檢查、審查

go（進行）＋ **over**（從頭到尾）＝ 從頭到尾進行

解說 此處的 over 是指「從頭到尾；全部」，類似用法有：read over（全部看過、讀過）、think over（仔細考慮），而 go over 則指「仔細檢查、審查」。

例
- Let's go over the details and find out where the mistake is.
  我們整個仔細檢查看到底哪裡出錯了。

註 go over 還有「講解說明」、「得到……的反應或評價」、「複習」等意思，需視上下文而定。

- Her performance went over very well.
  她的表演大受好評。

---

❻ go wrong   出差錯；發生故障

go（進行）＋ **wrong**（錯誤地）＝ 錯誤地進行

解說 wrong 在此作副詞用，意思是「錯誤地」。go wrong 除指「出差錯」外，還可表示「（機器）發生故障」、「（事情）不順利」等。

例
- If you always try your best, then there's no way you can go wrong.
  如果你總是全力以赴，就絕不會出錯。

反 go right 進行順利；成功

註 go wrong 為固定用法，其中的 wrong 不可用 wrongly 代替。

阻礙 Obstacles

❼ check up on　調查；檢查

check（調查；檢查）＋ **up**（作強調用）＋ **on**（針對）＝ 對……作調查、檢查

解說　check up on 常用在「調查」人的背景、行為等，以及事情是否屬實或有沒有問題。

例
- Employers should always check up on the background of possible employees.
  雇主在雇用員工之前一定要調查其背景。

似　check on/over 調查；檢查

❽ interfere with　阻礙；妨礙

interfere（阻礙）＋ **with**（與……在一起）＝ 對……形成阻礙

解說　interfere「阻礙；妨礙」為不及物動詞，若要加受詞，則必須在受詞前加上介系詞 with 或 in。

例
- The noise outside interfered with my sleep.
  外面的噪音干擾我的睡眠。

比　interfere in 干涉；干擾
- Please don't interfere in this matter.
  請別干涉這件事。

❾ be in the/one's way　造成阻礙

be in（在……中）＋ **the/one's way**（去路）＝ 在某人的去路上

解說　此語利用「同時佔用某人的去路」來形容「對……造成阻礙」，其中的 be 可用 get 取代。

例
- Don't let anyone or anything get in the way of your dreams.
  別讓任何人或任何事阻礙你實現夢想。

聯　get out of the way 讓開；別擋路

---

❿ make waves　引起騷動；惹是生非

make（引起）＋ **waves**（波動）＝ 引起水波

解說　此語利用「引起水波」的意象，引申指「引起騷動」。

例
- You can do whatever you want as long as you don't make waves here.
  只要你不在這裡惹是生非，你要做什麼都行。

似　rock the boat 興風作浪

活用狄克生片語　Lesson 25 複習測驗

一、選擇題（請選出一個最適當的選項）

1. I couldn't buy a drink because the machine was _____.
   (A) up to date　　(B) out of date　　(C) out of order　　(D) checked up on

2. Our cats destroyed everything in the house, so we _____ them.
   (A) got rid of　　(B) checked up on　(C) sell out　　(D) went over

3. I would have gotten to work on time _____ the rain and traffic.
   (A) in case of　　(B) but for　　(C) as to　　(D) as for

4. Before I gave the teacher my report, I _____ it very carefully.
   (A) checked up on　(B) went over　　(C) looked out fot　(D) looked for

二、翻譯填空

1. 我做了許多計畫要讓我的演出大為成功，但一切都出差錯。
   I made a lot of plans to make my performance a great one, but everything _____ _____.

2. 閃亮燈光的阻礙讓我看不清朝我飛來的棒球。
   The bright light _____ me _____ seeing the baseball coming at me.

3. 我父母到我就讀的大學來看看我過得怎麼樣。
   My parents came to my university to _____ _____ _____ how I was doing.

三、中翻英

1. 我父母告訴我他們絕不會干涉我未來的夢想和計畫。

   _____

2. 別給父母惹麻煩，就照他們說的去做。

   _____

3. 當我正試著做某件事時，我不喜歡別人妨礙我。

   _____

解答請參閱第273頁

Notes

Lesson 26

警覺 Paying Attention

Track 26

It's not easy being a crossing guard at school. You always have to be on your toes[1] and watch for kids who are in a hurry[2] and don't pay attention to[3] the rules.

It can be hard having to keep an eye on[4] all those little ones running in both directions and trying to get across the street before the time runs out. And many other things can turn up[5] and take you by surprise,[6] too. If you don't keep track of[7] the kids, they can get lost.

Sometimes you have to help them look for[8] their moms and dads. You have to look out[9] for cars and motorcycles that turn suddenly into the street. It's really stressful and a big responsibility.

My husband keeps telling me that I should see about[10] getting a new job, but I wouldn't change jobs for the world.

Lesson 26

❶ on one's toes　提高警覺的；準備好的

on（用）＋ **one's toes**（某人的腳趾）＝ 踮著腳尖

解說　原指運動選手在比賽時「踮著腳尖」以利快速移動或隨時出擊，現常用來形容人「提高警覺的；準備好的」。

例
- The team's constant practice keeps the players on their toes.
  該球隊持續不斷地練習，讓球員隨時做好比賽的準備。

---

❷ in a hurry　匆忙地；急忙地

in（在……狀態）＋ **a hurry**（匆忙）＝ 匆忙地

解說　雖然名詞 hurry「匆忙」並不可數，但 in a hurry「匆忙地；急忙地」已成為固定用法，其中的冠詞 a 不可省略。

例
- I'm in a hurry; can we talk about this tomorrow?
  我趕時間，我們可以明天再談嗎？

反　in no hurry 從容不迫；不急

警覺 Paying Attention

❸ pay attention (to)　注意;專心

pay（付出）**+ attention**（注意力）**=** 付出注意力

解說　常以「pay attention + to 名詞／動名詞」句型出現,表示「留心、注意……」,由於其中的 to 為介系詞,因此後面要接名詞或動名詞。

例
- We should always pay attention to customer feedback.
我們永遠必須留意顧客的反應。

似　take note of 注意;留心

---

❹ keep an eye on　留意

keep（保持）**+ an eye**（注視）**+ on**（在……上）**=** 留意……

解說　這裡的 eye 抽象地指「注視」,在使用上必須用單數,因此 keep an eye on 即為「注意;留心」之意。

例
- Joan asked her neighbor to keep an eye on her son while she ran an errand.
瓊安要求鄰居在她出去辦事時,幫她看一下兒子。

同　keep an eye out for 留意

聯　keep a close eye on 密切注意

Lesson 26

❺ turn up　增強;出現

turn（轉變）**+ up**（增加;出現）**=** 增強;出現

解說　turn up 除指「增強」外,亦常形容人「突然露面、現身」,或表示「(某物)意外被尋獲」,但不論形容人或物都必須用主動語態。

例
- Please turn up the volume!
  請開大聲一點!
- Joe invited Jane to dinner, but she didn't turn up.
  喬約珍吃晚餐,但她卻沒有出現。
- I hope my lost wallet turns up soon.
  我希望我掉的皮包可以早日尋獲。

似　show up 出現;現身

---

❻ take by surprise　出其不意;使……驚訝

take（捉拿）**+ by**（藉由）**+ surprise**（驚訝）**=** 使……驚訝

解說　常以「take + 人 + by surprise」來表示「在某人毫無準備的情況下,出其不意地讓他驚喜或讓他措手不及」。

例
- The promotion took Jill by surprise.
  吉兒對於被升職感到很意外。

同　「catch + 人 + by surprise」出其不意;使……驚訝

警覺 Paying Attention

❼ keep track of　追蹤；密切注意

keep（保持）＋ **track**（蹤跡）＋ **of**（動作的對象）＝ 追蹤……的蹤跡

解說　keep track of 除指「追蹤」外，亦可引申指「密切注意……」。

例
- Teachers must keep track of every student while they are on field trips.
  校外教學時，老師必須非常注意每個學生。

聯　lose track of 失去線索、消息

❽ look for　尋找

look（注意看）＋ **for**（為了）＝ 尋找

解說　look for 字面意思是「為了……而仔細查看」，即「尋找；尋求」之意。

例
- I found the books I've been looking for.
  我找到了我一直在找的書。

比　look for 和 find 在中文的意思都是「找」，但 look for 強調「尋找」的過程，而 find 則強調結果，也就是「找到」。

❾ look out　小心；留心

look（注意看）＋ **out**（完全地）＝ 小心；留心

解說　look out 常用來提醒別人要「小心；留心」，而「look out for + 壞事／壞人」則指「小心……」，例如：Look out for pickpockets.（小心扒手）。

例
- Look out! Don't fall into that hole!
  小心！別掉進那個洞裡！

註1　look out 雖有「向外看；眺望」的意思，但通常會在後面加上介系詞 at 或 of，如：look out at（眺望……）、look out of（由……朝外看）。但碰到像 look out (of) the window（看窗外）這種可省略 of 的情況，要請讀者特別注意，別把意思弄混了。

註2　「look out for + 人」亦可當「照顧」解，例如：

- My older brother always looks out for me.
  我哥哥總是很照顧我。

---

❿ see about　留意；安排

see（關心）＋ **about**（關於）＝ 留意；安排

解說　常以「see about + 事物／V-ing」表示「留意；處理；安排；進一步考慮」某事物。

例
- If mom's busy, I'll see about cooking dinner.
  如果老媽忙的話，晚餐就由我來料理。

聯1 we'll have to see about that 這我們可要看看（也就是現在不能決定）

聯2 we'll (soon) see about that 我們走著瞧

活用狄克生片語　Lesson 26 複習測驗

一、選擇題（請選出一個最適當的選項）

1. When you play basketball, you always need to _____ or you'll miss something.
   (A) be on your toes
   (B) take by surprise
   (C) keep your eyes on
   (D) pay attention to

2. People in the city are always _____ to get from one place to another.
   (A) in no hurry　　(B) in a hurry　　(C) at once　　(D) in no time

3. If you don't _____ the traffic rules, you could get hurt.
   (A) pay attention　(B) pay attention to　(C) look out　(D) look out for

4. Always _____ your kids when you take them out.
   (A) be on your toes　(B) look out　(C) keep eyes on　(D) keep an eye on

二、翻譯填空

1. 要密切注意所有我今晚新認識的人真難。
   It's hard to _____ _____ _____ all the new people I met tonight.

2. 我餵食一隻流浪狗，隔天就有另外十隻出現在我家門口。
   I fed a stray dog and ten other dogs _____ _____ at my door the next day.

3. 當我畢業，我打算要在台灣這裡的美國公司找個職務。
   When I graduate, I want to _____ _____ getting a position in an American company here in Taiwan.

三、中翻英

1. 我想找份可運用我數學及科學技能的工作。

   _____

2. 我父母教導我要留心那些可能試著佔我便宜的人。

   _____

3. 我不知道你們要為我舉辦派對，這讓我感到很意外。

   _____

Lesson 27

判別 Differences

Track 27

When I moved abroad to go to school, I found living in another country was a far cry from[1] living at home. First, I got lost all the time. The street signs looked all the same![2] I soon knew my surroundings by sight;[3] it was the only way I could find my dorm. I'm not good at directions anyway. I guess I take after[4] my father that way.

Also, to be honest, I felt a little sickened at the sight of[5] the food there. But I tried my best to cut down on[6] eating food from back home. I wanted to experience life like the people in my new home.

The first day I went to the office to look into[7] making some changes in my classes. In the office I couldn't tell one person from[8] another. One nice lady looked over[9] my information and then walked away. Another lady in the office came and asked me a question, but I took her for[10] the first lady! It was really embarrassing.

Lesson 27

❶ be a far cry from　　與……大為不同

be a（是一個）＋ **far**（遠的）＋ **cry**（喊叫）＋ **from**（從）
＝ 以喊叫聲測距離

解說　此語原指「以喊叫聲來測量遠處敵人的位置」，後來引申為「與……大為不同」。

例
- This color is a far cry from what I asked for.
  這顏色和我要的大為不同。

❷ all the same　　完全一樣；儘管如此

all（全部）＋ **the same**（一樣）＝ 完全一樣

解說　all the same 除字面意思「完全一樣」外，亦可表示「儘管如此；還是」。

例
- It's all the same as last month because we haven't heard what to change or add.
  和上個月完全一樣，因為我們沒聽說要有所改變或增加。

- I know he's a bad boy, but I love him all the same.
  我知道他是個壞男孩，但我還是愛他。

判別 Differences

❸ know by sight　認得；見過面

know（認出）+ **by**（藉由）+ **sight**（視覺）= 認得；見過面

解說　「know + 人 + by sight」是指「認得；見過面」，但並非真的認識。但 know 後面若加事物，則表示「認得出」某事物。

例
- I don't really know him, but I know him by sight.
  我實際上並不認識他，但我認得他。

❹ take after　與……相像

take（獲得）+ **after**（仿照）= 仿照某人

解說　「take after + 父母／親戚」是指孩子在長相或行為上「與……相像」。

例
- Jenny really takes after her mother.
  珍妮非常像她的母親。

❺ at the sight of　一看見……就

at（一……）+ **the sight**（看見）+ **of**（行為的對象）= 一看見……就

解說　此處的 at 用來表示原因，指「因為看到、聽到或其他動作而立即有……的反應」，因此 at the sight of 的意思是「一看見……就」。

[例] • I faint at the sight of blood.
我一看到血就會昏倒。

❻ cut down on　減少；削減

cut（削減）+ **down**（減少）+ **on**（針對）= 減少；削減

[解說]　「cut down on + 事物」用來表示「減少……的數量；減少使用……」。

[例] • Cutting down on sugar in your diet is good for your health.
減少糖分的攝取量對健康有益。

[似]　cut back on 減少；削減

[比]　cut down 亦可指「減少；削減」，但通常必須明確指出是哪些事物或對象，舉例來說：

• I need to cut down the time I spend looking for information.
我必須減少找資料的時間。

• This article is too long, it needs to be cut down before we can publish it.
這篇文章太長，必須經過刪節才能刊登。

判別 Differences

❼ look into　調查

look（看）+ **into**（進入……之內）= 朝……裡面看

解說　look into 除字面意思「朝……裡面看」外，常引申指「調查」事物的原因、內幕等。

例
- I've looked into it and learned that the problems are due to new security measures.
  我調查後發現問題出在新的安檢措施。

---

❽ tell from　辨別　（可分開片語）

tell（辨別）+ **from**（有別於）= 辨別

解說　常以「tell + A + from + B」句型表示「分辨 A 和 B 的差別」。

例
- The twins are so alike, I can hardly tell one from the other.
  這對雙胞胎長得很像，我實在分不出誰是誰。

同　「tell the difference between A and B」意思是「分辨 A 和 B 之間的差別」

似　「tell + 人／事物 + apart」亦表示「辨別」，但所要分辨的人或事物要放在片語中間。

- The twins are so alike, I can hardly tell them apart.
  這對雙胞胎長得很像，我實在分不出誰是誰。

225

Lesson 27

❾ look over　檢視；過目　可分開片語

look（看）＋ over（全面地）＝ 全面地看

解說　look over 通常用來表示「很快地檢視、掃瞄或觀察」。

例
- Please look over this fax before I send it.
  這張傳真在寄出去前，請幫我過目一下。

❿ take for　將……視為；將……誤認為

take（接受）＋ for（代替）＝ 將……視為；將……誤認為

解說　常以「take + A + for + B」句型表示「將……視為；將……誤認為」。

例
- Don't take me for a fool.
  別把我當作傻瓜。

- I took him for Mr. Brown.
  我把他誤認成布朗先生。

似　「mistake + A + for + B」是指「把 A 誤認成 B」，也可用被動態「A + be mistaken + for + B」表示「A 被誤認成 B」。

- Tod was mistaken for his father when he answered the phone.
  陶德接電話時被誤認成他爸爸。

活用狄克生片語　Lesson 27 複習測驗

一、選擇題（請選出一個最適當的選項）

1. My recent test performance ＿＿＿＿＿＿ my failing grades in the past.
   (A) is a far cry from (B) gets even with (C) takes for (D) takes after

2. I don't understand modern art; it ＿＿＿＿＿ to me.
   (A) gets through (B) give way (C) looks all the same (D) runs up

3. After I studied tea for a while, I knew the different kinds ＿＿＿＿＿.
   (A) out of sight (B) in sight (C) at the sight (D) by sight

4. My father is very good at math, so I ＿＿＿＿ him because I'm good at it, too.
   (A) take after (B) take care of (C) look after (D) look over

二、翻譯填空

1. 起初我老師似乎太嚴格了，事實上，我誤以為她是一個嚴格的人。
   At first my teacher seemed too serious when I first met her; in fact, I ＿＿＿＿ ＿＿＿＿ ＿＿＿＿ a strict person.

2. 她應該減少飯量，因為她體重增加太快了。
   She should ＿＿＿＿ ＿＿＿＿ ＿＿＿＿ her meals because she's gaining so much weight.

3. 我必須查一下我出國要花多少錢。
   I need to ＿＿＿＿ ＿＿＿＿ how much money I'll need to travel abroad.

三、中翻英

1. 這兩個盒子看起來很像，我無法分辨哪個是哪個。

2. 我小時候總是習慣要求我父親檢視我的家庭作業。

3. 我絕不可能當醫生，因為我一看到血就暈了。

Notes

Lesson 28

管控 In Charge

Track 28

My best friend from high school Bud and I decided we could make use of[1] the Internet to start our own business. We really didn't know what we were doing, but we knew if we could play it by ear,[2] we could get away with[3] almost anything.

We started our computer repair business and I was in charge of[4] the office. I knew I could count on[5] Bud to do the repairs because he would always take pains[6] to keep up with the latest technology.

I wanted to have beautiful offices, but we had to make do[7] with a cheap storefront. Bud wanted a great laboratory, so we met halfway[8] and he got a workbench.

We would suggest that anyone who wants to work for themselves take up[9] a hobby instead! Because in the real world, not everything you think is in your control is actually in hand![10]

Lesson 28

❶ make use of　利用

make（做）+ **use**（利用）+ **of**（動作對象）= 利用

解說　常以「make（good/better）+ use of + 人／事物」表示「（好好）利用……」。

例
- Making good use of public transportation can save time during rush hour.
  善加利用大眾運輸在尖峰時間可節省時間。

似　**take advantage of** 利用；佔……的便宜

- Take advantage of the special offer and save big on your power bill.
  利用這次優惠可幫你省下大筆電費。

---

❷ play by ear　憑印象演奏；見機行事

play（演奏）+ **by**（憑藉）+ **ear**（耳朵）= 不看樂譜演奏

解說　「play + 事物 + by ear」原指「憑聽過的印象，不看樂譜演奏音樂」，如今常引申指「見機行事」。

例
- We have no plan. We'll have to play it by ear.
  我們沒有計畫，必須見機行事。

管控 In Charge

❸ get away with　成功過關;逃過懲罰

get（得到）**+ away**（遠離）**+ with**（與……一起）**=** 與……一起逃離

解說　「get away with + 壞事／錯事」常用來形容做壞事或錯事而未受懲罰、責罵或被發覺。

例
- Melissa gets away with not studying because she is naturally good at math.
  梅麗莎因為天生數學好,就算不讀書也能過關。

❹ be in charge of　管理;負責

be in（在……中）**+ charge**（管理）**+ of**（行為對象）**=** 管理、負責……

解說　「be in charge of + 名詞／動名詞」是指「負責……;掌管……」,主詞多為人或機構。

例
- Susan is in charge of the sales department.
  蘇珊掌管業務部。

似　take charge of 管理;負責

聯　「put + 人 + in charge of」意思是「讓某人管理、負責……」

❺ count on　依靠；仰賴

count（計算）+ **on**（在……上）= 算在……上

解說　常以下列句型「count on + 人 + 不定詞／動名詞／for 事物」表示「可依靠、仰賴某人……」。

例
- Customers count on us to provide quality products.
  顧客仰賴我們提供優質產品。

似　depend on、rely on「依靠；仰賴」

註　count on 亦可指「預期（某事發生）」，常用來表達說話者認定某事一定會發生。
- You can count on Tony being late for the meeting!
  湯尼開會鐵定會遲到！

❻ take pains　不辭辛勞；費盡苦心

take（承擔）+ **pains**（辛勞）= 不辭辛勞

解說　pain 除指「疼痛」外，亦有「辛勞」之意，例如：No pain, no gain.（不勞則無獲），因此，take pains 是指「不辭辛勞；費盡苦心」以完成某事。常可在 pains 前加形容詞 great 以強調「極為盡心盡力」。

例
- I should thank Ellen. She took great pains to help me.
  我應該謝謝愛倫，她非常盡心盡力地幫我。

似　be at pains、go to (great) pains「不辭辛勞；費盡苦心」

管控 In Charge

註 常以「take (great) pains + 不定詞」句型出現。

---

❼ make do　　將就；權宜之計

make（讓）**+ do**（完成）**=** 讓……完成

解說　常用來表示在現有資源、人力等不足的情況下，設法處理或完成某事，常以「make do + with/without 人／事物」句型出現。

例
- Our cable isn't installed yet; we'll have to make do with watching DVDs.
  我們的纜線還沒裝好，只好看 DVD 將就一下。

- Tom isn't here, so we'll have to make do without him.
  湯姆不在，所以我們得在沒有他的情況下想辦法應付。

---

❽ meet (someone) halfway　　妥協；讓步

meet（迎接）**+ someone**（某人）**+ halfway**（中途）**=** 在中途迎接某人

解說　此語利用「在中途迎接某人」來比喻「與某人妥協」。

例
- You two have to learn to meet halfway.
  你們倆得學會妥協。

Lesson 28

- Jane wanted a 50 percent discount, but the salesperson agreed to meet her halfway and gave her 25 percent off.
  珍要求打對折，但業務員同意讓步，給她打七五折。

同 go halfway 妥協；讓步

---

❾ take up　開始；著手進行　可分開片語

take（拿）＋ **up**（起來）＝ 著手做

解說　這個片語隨著 take 意思的不同而產生許多不同的意思，舉例來說：take 若作「吸收」、「接受」、「佔有」解，take up 便有「吸收；攝取」、「接受」、「佔用」的意思。在這裡，take up 是指「開始；著手進行」，常用於活動、工作、嗜好等。

例
- Jason took up tennis to get fit.
  傑生開始打網球健身。

---

❿ in hand　在掌握之中

in（在……中）＋ **hand**（手）＝ 在手中

解說　in hand 字面意思是「在手中」，引申指「在掌握之中」，相當於 under control。

管控 In Charge

例
- Don't worry. I have everything well in hand; the food will be ready soon.
  別擔心,一切都在我的掌握之中;飯很快就可以吃了。

聯 in one's hands 由某人負責、處理

反 out of hand 失控(但此語亦可作「當場;立即」解)

活用狄克生片語　Lesson 28 複習測驗

一、選擇題（請選出一個最適當的選項）

1. I want to_____ my college education in a field I can enjoy.
   (A) take up　　(B) make use of　　(C) get away with　　(D) take pains with

2. We don't have any specific plans for tonight, so let's just _____.
   (A) meet halfway　(B) take it in hand　(C) do it by hand　(D) play it by ear

3. He's the teacher's favorite student, so he can _____ anything.
   (A) get away with　(B) make do with　(C) play up to　(D) count on

4. When her parents are at work, she is _____ her younger sister.
   (A) in hand with　(B) getting away with　(C) meeting halfway　(D) in charge of

二、翻譯填空

1. 我要求我老闆給我大幅加薪，他說他願意折中一下，給我小幅調薪。
   I asked my boss for a big raise, he said he would _____ _____ _____ and give me a small one.

2. 她是個漂亮的女孩，總是費盡心思呈現自己最美的一面。
   She's a beautiful girl and always _____ _____ to look her best.

3. 在購物中心，這位母親必須持續掌控她的四個小孩。
   The mother had to keep her four children _____ _____ at the mall.

三、中翻英

1. 你總是能信守承諾，所以我知道我可以仰賴你。

   _____

2. 我父親退休了，決定開始培養釣魚作為新嗜好。

   _____

3. 我很想要一台BMW，但我必須將就開一台福特，因為比較便宜。

   _____

Lesson 29

時程 Scheduling

During the busy season we always fall behind[1] in our work. The trick is to catch up[2] little by little.[3] If you don't, it's all a lost cause![4]

Just to keep up with the work, we have to do without[5] holidays! My boss said he wanted to do away with[6] lunch hours, too, but I said I thought it might be best to put off[7] deciding that till later.

If we can start a project in time[8] to meet deadlines and keep it on schedule,[9] we have a chance to get it finished on time, too.

Once finished, we sometimes want to hold it over[10] so other prospective customers can see what quality work we do.

Lesson 29

❶ fall behind　落後

fall（落到）＋ **behind**（在……之後）＝ 落後

解說　fall behind 除可單獨使用外，「fall behind + 人」是指「落後某人」，「fall behind + with + 事物」是指「在……上落後」。

例
- The student was often absent, so he fell behind.
  這學生常缺席，所以功課就落後了。

同　get behind、lag behind「落後」

聯1　a step behind 落後別人一步

聯2　fall behind schedule 進度落後

---

❷ catch up　趕上；追上

catch（趕上）＋ **up**（完全地）＝ 趕上

解說　常以「catch up + with + 人／事物」句型表示「趕上……」。

例
- I ran down the road, hoping to catch up with the bus at the traffic light.
  我一路跑過去，希望能在紅綠燈附近趕上公車。

比　catch up on 趕完、彌補（耽擱下的工作、學習、睡眠等）

- I think I should catch up on some sleep.
  我想我應該要補一下眠。

註　catch up 亦可指「聊聊近況」（通常用於許久未見的朋友身上）

- We have to sit down and catch up on old times.
  我們可得坐下來聊聊過往。

❸ little by little　逐漸地

little（一點點）+ **by**（接著）+ **little**（一點點）= 一點一點地

解說　此處 by 的意思是「逐漸；接著」，常見用法有 one by one（一個接一個）、step by step（一步步）、day by day（一天天）等，因此 little by little 是指「逐漸地」。

例
- Little by little I became more fluent in English.
  漸漸地，我的英文變得更流利。

❹ a lost cause　毫無希望

a（一）+ **lost**（輸了的）+ **cause**（訴訟）= 一場輸了的官司

解說　此語藉由「一場輸了的官司」來比喻事情或狀況等「毫無希望」。

例
- I never lose weight; my dieting is a lost cause.
  我體重根本沒減輕，我進行節食一點用也沒有。

似　a losing battle 必敗無疑

Lesson 29

❺ do without 沒有……也行；沒有……而將就

do（做）+ **without**（沒有）= 沒有……照樣進行

[解說] do without 是指「沒有……也行；沒有……而將就」，但前面若接了否定詞 cannot、can't，則表示「沒有……不行；少不了……」。

[例]
- Terry forgot to bring the CDs to the party, so we had to do without.
  泰瑞忘了帶 CD 唱片來派對，所以我們只好將就點了。

- When you go to the beach, sunscreen is something you can't do without.
  去海灘時，沒帶防曬油是不行的。

[註] 「can/could do without + 事物」並不能照字面解讀，常用來表示某事物「造成困擾或麻煩」。

- I could do without all that noise outside.
  外面的噪音實在很吵。

---

❻ do away with 廢除；除去；擺脫

do（執行）+ **away**（遠離）+ **with**（與……一地）= 除去；擺脫

[解說] 常以「do away with + 事物」表示「廢止；除去；擺脫」某事物；而「do away with + 人」則指「將人殺死」，屬於俚俗用法，相當於中文的「做掉」。

時程 Scheduling

例
- Legislators did away with the unpopular law.
  立法委員們廢除了這條不受歡迎的法令。

- The gangster did away with his rivals.
  該名黑道份子做掉了他的對手。

似　get rid of 去除；擺脫

---

❼ put off　拖延；延遲 〔可分開片語〕

put（放）＋ **off**（離開地）＝ 往較遠的時間點放

解說　put off 是指將原本預定的時程向後「拖延；延遲」。

例
- Never put off until tomorrow what you can do today.
  今日事今日畢。

似　delay、postpone 拖延

註1　亦常以「put off + V-ing」句型出現。

- Jenny kept putting off cleaning her aquarium.
  珍妮一直拖延不清理她的水族箱。

註2　若使用的對象為人，常以「put + 人 + off」句型表示「使人反感、喪失意願或興趣」。

- Tony got bitten by a dog when he was little, and this put him off dogs for life.
  湯尼小時候曾被狗咬，這讓他一輩子都討厭狗。

❽ in time 及時；來得及

in（在……內）+ **time**（時限）= 在時限內

解說　這裡的 time 是指 time limit「時限」，而 in time 則表示「及時；來得及」。

例
- I was just in time for the 7:00 train.
  我剛好來得及趕上七點的火車。

註　time 若解作「時間」，則 in time 是指「遲早；終將；總有一天」。

- They'll see in time that I was right.
  他們終究會明白，我是對的。

聯　on time 準時

---

❾ on schedule 按照預定時間；準時

on（在……上）+ **schedule**（時刻表）= 在火車時刻表上

解說　原指依照所刊印的火車時刻表發車，如今常引申指「按照預定時間；準時」。

例
- Your flight will depart on schedule at gate ten.
  您的班機將在十號門準時起飛。

聯　ahead of schedule（較預定時間提前）、behind schedule（較預定時間落後）

時程 Scheduling

⑩ hold over　延長；延期　(可分開片語)

hold（保持）＋ over（超過）＝ 維持超過

解說　為常見的美式用語，常以被動語態 be held over 表示影片、戲劇等由於太過賣座，而「延長」放映的期限。

例
- The theater just announced they will hold the film over for another week.
  戲院剛才宣布，該片將續映一週。

活用狄克生片語 Lesson 29 複習測驗

一、選擇題（請選出一個最適當的選項）

1. He was sick for a month and _____ in his schoolwork.
   (A) held over　　(B) fell behind　　(C) took pains　　(D) did well

2. Stop trying to help that lazy student because it's _____.
   (A) a lost cause　　(B) a lost match　　(C) a hold over　　(D) a big game

3. Most people would like to _____ housework.
   (A) get away with　(B) make do with　(C) do away with　(D) count on

4. You should never _____ important work for your boss.
   (A) fall behind　　(B) catch on　　(C) do without　　(D) put off

二、翻譯填空

1. 她說她沒有手機不行。
   She says she cannot _____ _____ her cell phone.

2. 起初，他不懂這個數學問題，但慢慢地，他還是能夠解出來。
   At first, he didn't understand the math problem, but _____ _____ _____, he was able to figure it out.

3. 我必須趕完我的家庭作業，因為我落後蠻多的。
   I have to _____ _____ _____ my homework because I'm so behind.

三、中翻英

1. 老師會把考試延到星期一。
   _____

2. 如果你不及時起床，你上學就會遲到。
   _____

3. 我們可以維持預訂進度。
   _____

Lesson 30

犯罪 Crimes

Track 30

Steve worked at a convenience store. He tells the story that one night on the late shift a guy came in with a gun and held up[1] the store. The thief tried to break into[2] the safe but couldn't, so he was going to blow it up.[3] Steve thought it would set fire to[4] the building and probably burn it down,[5] so he told him the safe had just been emptied.

The guy let go of[6] his gun. When it hit the floor, it went off and hit a box of cigarette lighters on the counter. The lighters caught fire and the stack of popcorn next to them started popping. The guy tried to tear up[7] his shirt and use that to put out[8] the fire, but it didn't work. He started apologizing and even asked where the first aid kit was!

So, we can't really say that the police put down[9] the robbery attempt. They said he probably wanted to get even with[10] the owner, not really hurt anyone.

Lesson 30

❶ hold up　持槍搶劫　〔可分開片語〕

hold（保持）＋ up（起來）＝ 把手舉起來

[解說]　此語源自搶匪持槍搶劫時,通常都會叫人「把手舉起來」,如今衍生指「持槍搶劫」。

[例]
- The bank was held up by masked gunmen.
  那間銀行遭蒙面歹徒持槍搶劫。

[衍]　holdup 為其名詞。
- There was a holdup at the gas station.
  這家加油站發生搶案。

❷ break into　闖入;侵入

break（破壞）＋ into（進入）＝ 闖入

[解說]　此語若用於犯罪時,通常是指「闖入;侵入」以進行偷竊。

[例]
- The police caught a burglar trying to break into our home.
  警方抓到一名竊賊試圖闖入我們家。

[註1]　break into 若用於好的方面,則指「成功打進」,例如:break into Hollywood（打進好萊塢）、break into the market（打進市場）等。

[註2]　break into 亦可指「突然……起來」,如:break into laughter/tears「突然笑了／哭了起來」。

犯罪 Crimes

❸ blow up　爆炸
可分開片語

blow（爆破）＋ **up**（完全地）＝ 爆炸

解說　blow up 有許多不同的意思，在此是指「完全爆破」，即「爆炸」之意。

例
- Terrorists threatened to blow up the plane.
恐怖份子威脅炸掉這架飛機。

註　「blow（吹氣）＋ up（起來）＝ 充氣」是 blow up 另一個常見的意思，常指為 ballon（氣球）、tire（輪胎）等「充氣；打氣」。

❹ set fire to　放火；焚燒

set（放）＋ **fire**（火）＋ **to**（對）＝ 對……放火

解說　常以「set fire to ＋ 事物」表示「放火；焚燒」。

例
- The Greeks lit the torches and set fire to the city of Troy.
希臘人點燃火炬，放火燒特洛伊城。

似　「set ＋ 事物 ＋ on fire」是指「縱火；讓……著火」。

❺ burn down　燒毀

可分開片語

burn（燃燒）+ **down**（徹底地）= 燒毀

解說　由於 down 本身還有「向下」的意思，因此 burn down 常指東西、建築物等「整個被燒毀只剩地上的殘破的碎片或瓦礫」。

例
- Our house burned down and now we have nowhere to go.
  我們的房子燒毀了，現在我們無處可去。

似　burn (something) to the ground 將……燒毀；把……燒個精光

❻ let go (of)　放開；釋放

let（讓）+ **go**（離開）+ **of**（分離）= 放開；釋放

解說　常以「let go of + 人／事物」、「let go + 人／事物」、「let + 人／事物 + go」三種句型表示「放開、釋放……」，但這裡的「人」主要是指「人的手或手臂等被抓住的部分」。此外，亦抽象地指對事情「放手不管」。

例
- Let go of my hand. You're hurting me!
  放開我的手，你弄痛我了！

- Sometimes you just have to learn to let go.
  有時，你就是得學會放手。

犯罪 Crimes

❼ tear up　撕裂；撕毀　（可分開片語）

tear（撕破）＋ **up**（完全地）＝ 撕裂；撕毀

解說　tear up 是指「將……撕成碎片」，也就是「撕裂；撕毀」。

例
- Jenny tore up the letter and threw it away.
  珍妮把信撕毀丟掉。

比　tear down 拆除；拆毀

---

❽ put out　熄滅；使不省人事　（可分開片語）

put（使朝向）＋ **out**（消失）＝ 熄滅；不省人事

解說　out 一般作「向外」解，但在此則指「消失」，類似用法如：blow out（吹熄）、run out（用光），而 put out 則指「熄滅；使不省人事」。

例
- The waiter asked Susan to put out her cigarette, because she was at a non-smoking table.
  服務生要求蘇珊將煙熄滅，因為她的座位是非吸煙區。

註　「put（推）＋ out（向外）＝ 推出；生產」是 put out 另一個常見的意思。

- Our company plans to put out a new product next year.
  我們公司計畫明年推出一項新產品。

Lesson 30

❾ put down　放下；鎮壓　可分開片語

put（放；使朝向）＋ **down**（向下）＝ 放下；鎮壓

解說　put down 除指「放下」外，亦可指對暴動、非法遊行等進行「鎮壓」，或「取締」犯罪等。

例
- Put down the gun and raise your hands.
  把槍放下，手舉起來。
- The riot was instantly put down by the police.
  這場暴動迅速遭警方鎮壓住。

❿ get even with　報復

get（使……）＋ **even**（相同的）＋ **with**（與……）＝ 與……扯平

解說　「get/be even with + 人」是用來表示「向某人報復；以其人之道還治其人之身」的意思。

例
- I'll get even with you one day.
  總有一天我會向你報復。

同　get revenge on 報復

活用狄克生片語　　Lesson 30 複習測驗

一、選擇題（請選出一個最適當的選項）

1. A thief _____ the convenience store in my neighborhood yesterday.
   (A) held up　　(B) let go of　　(C) tore up　　(D) put out

2. This house is almost impossible to _____.
   (A) break down　　(B) break into　　(C) break up　　(D) break off

3. The criminal wanted to take a bomb to the bank and _____.
   (A) put it up　　(B) put it out　　(C) tear it up　　(D) blow it up

4. While he was playing with a candle, the little boy _____ the house.
   (A) put out　　(B) let go of　　(C) set fire to　　(D) held up

二、翻譯填空

1. 湯尼對他考試的成績很生氣，他把試卷給撕了丟到垃圾桶。
   Tony was so upset with his test score, he _____ _____ his test and threw it in the trash can.

2. 去年一場大火將這圖書館整個燒毀了。
   There was a terrible fire last year and the library _____ _____.

3. 有些火災實在太大，要一兩天才能完全撲滅。
   Some fires are so big, it takes a day or two before they can be _____ _____ completely.

三、中翻英

1. 如果有人傷害你，很自然的會想要進行報復。
   _____

2. 警方在很短的時間內鎮壓了這起暴動。
   _____

3. 這小孩拒絕放開他的糖果。
   _____

解答請參閱第277頁

Translation 中文翻譯

Lesson 1: Eating 飲食

我爸爸老是告訴我:「女朋友總想上餐館;老婆總想在家吃。」我想追一位女朋友,她名字叫汪達。於是,我請她去吃一頓燭光晚餐。

在餐廳裡,當服務我們的人員將餐點送上來時,我想要幫汪達盛菜,但汪達說要自己來,然後就把食物吃光。

汪達是一位非常時髦的女孩,我想向汪達表現出自己也很時髦。

但這時事情發生了。汪達滿嘴食物,她突然看著我說:「這食物有肉的味道。」汪達說她不吃肉,覺得想吐。

我想時髦女孩是不吃肉的。

服務生清理乾淨後,便把帳單送來,這是我最後向汪達表現我很時髦的機會,於是我建議由她來付帳,這令她十分生氣,接著我建議我們各付各的。

我想這很公平,因為我只吃了一半的食物。

之後她再也沒跟我說過話。

Answer Key 解答

一、1. (B) 2. (A) 3. (C) 4. (D)

二、1. tastes of 2. cleaning up 3. like throwing up

三、1. During Chinese New Year, my mother dishes delicious soup out to all our family.

2. Unlike the Chinese tradition, Westerners ask their guests to help themselves at dinner.

3. Chinese enjoy hospitality and often wait on their guests happily.

一式搞定狄克生片語　**Translation** 中文翻譯

Lesson 2: Dressing 服飾穿著

我男朋友不懂流行，他的褲子和鞋子都穿壞了，他不喜歡盛裝打扮穿好的衣服，當他衣服髒了，他就把衣服反過來，就那樣穿著。

有一天我們走在市區，女孩子們嘲笑他，說他穿得像個雞農。

他雖然不在乎，但我覺得很丟臉，我決定讓他跟上最新潮流。

我帶他去一些時尚店，要他脫掉他那些遜斃了的衣服，我要他試穿酷炫的褲子。因為褲子太大了，所以銷售員就把它們改小，看起來很完美。

然後我挑選了一些有型的鞋子和顏色鮮豔的襯衫，我讓他穿上這些衣服。當我一切搞定後，他完全跟上最新潮流。

我男朋友說他不在乎，但是我在乎。

稍後，我們又遇到了那些女孩。這次，她們並沒有嘲笑他，她們對他微笑，我男朋友也對她們微笑。

現在一切都不一樣了，我的男朋友變得非常時髦。

或許這就是為什麼我們離開城市，搬到鄉下，開了一家養雞場。

Answer Key 解答

一、1. (A)　2. (C)　3. (C)　4. (B)

二、1. dress up　2. are in　3. take in

三、1. How do you know it fits if you don't try it on?

　　2. When I come home from school, I take off my uniform and relax.

　　3. The first time I put on my heavy bookbag, I almost fell down.

Translation 中文翻譯

Lesson 3: Family Life 居家生活

週末我通常都待在家，偶而會有一、兩個朋友順道來訪。這可能令人覺得寂寞，但過一陣子就會逐漸習慣。

這並不是我媽的錯，她扶養我長大要我循規蹈矩，但我卻沒有。

我父母並沒有要求我作太多家事，但有一次他們要求我整理玄關的衣櫃並把我所有的衣服收好。

可是那天早上我一直睡到快十一點才起床，而且我想要為我即將去歐洲度假三個禮拜的好友送行。

當我梳好頭髮、化好妝，就已經沒時間整理衣櫃或收拾我的東西，她們交代我的事，我一件都沒做就離開家裡。

我想我必須同意他們的做法，我應該要被禁足一個月。

Answer Key 解答

一、1. (B) 2. (A) 3. (C) 4. (A)

二、1. cleaned out 2. put on/makeup 3. get up/catch

三、1. My grandmother always gets sad when she sees us off after holidays.

2. After my family eats, my sisters have to put away all the dishes.

3. My parents brought me up to be a good citizen.

Lesson 4: Driving 開車

比利·賓恩是一位冰淇淋車駕駛。當孩子們聽到他貨車上播放的歌曲便會為之瘋狂。可是比利討厭小孩，覺得他們只想吃他的冰淇淋。

Translation 中文翻譯

他的朋友就只有他的狗「卡蘇」，還有我。比利開車時，卡蘇會坐在比利旁邊，舔著莓果香蕉冰淇淋，而我討厭吃冰淇淋。

有一天，比利的狗走失了，它在比利卸下一些冰淇淋到商店時跑掉了。

貨車開到我家，比利告訴我怎麼一回事。他在車上為我挪出空位，要我上車。

冰淇淋貨車歌曲開始播放，小孩子們跑了過來。比利覺得生氣並快速倒車，因為他們試圖上車。

卡蘇也想要跳上貨車，我試著告訴比利放慢速度，但他卻直接輾過了卡蘇。

這也就是為什麼現在比利不再賣莓果香蕉冰淇淋，也不再播放冰淇淋貨車歌曲的原因。

前幾天我恰巧遇到他，現在他開貨車經過附近時都放緩且輕聲地開。

Answer Key 解答

一、1. (A) 2. (C) 3. (D) 4. (C)

二、1. got in 2. backed up 3. get on

三、1. If my friends drive too fast and won't slow down, I never ride with them again.

2. Yesterday I ran over a small bird in the road.

3. It always makes me happy to run into my teachers from elementary school.

Lesson 5: Trips 旅遊

我爸有時會帶著我們一起出差，他不期望出差，但我們卻很期待，這對我哥和我來說，是玩樂的好時機。

旅程開始我們就很興奮。

Translation 中文翻譯

當他在打包西裝以及文件資料時,我們就打包我們的泳衣,這是我們唯一需要的東西。

到了機場,我哥和我排隊並爭著看誰要坐窗邊。辦好住房登記後,我們就去游泳池,在旅館游泳池游泳最棒了。當我爸努力工作時,我們就放輕鬆還去健身。

我知道我爸是有些難過,因為他沒辦法休假,沒辦法加入我們的玩樂,但是他還是很高興看到我們玩得開心。

Answer Key 解答

一、1. (A) 2. (D) 3. (C) 4. (C)

二、1. check in 2. take part in 3. having a good time

三、1. I often take time off from work to read interesting books.

   2. Vacation is a time to take it easy and enjoy life.

   3. I'm healthy because I take the time to work out three times a week.

Lesson 6: Learning 學習

我上學讀書的時間很長,我朋友都笑我主修「學校」。

每天晚上我都會熬夜,為的就是把隔天的指定作業都讀一遍,我會把課文背起來,也都會準時交家庭作業。

大學跟高中大為不同,有很多事情弄清楚,你必須很快學會訣竅,當老師點名時,你最好是在座位上,準備好要上課。

你不能老是遲到,如果你不相信我說的,用你字典查「退學」這個字,而這次不要用你的電子辭典,要用真的字典。

Translation 中文翻譯

你該不會想要跟書本疏遠吧,因為接下來的四年,他們將是你最好的朋友。

Answer Key 解答

一、1. (A) 2. (B) 3. (D) 4. (C)

二、1. called the roll 2. foreign/ look up 3. lose your touch

三、1. The teacher asked us to hand in our homework from last week.

2. I was the first person in my class to figure out the math problem.

3. After you have worked here for a while, you'll learn the ropes.

Lesson 7: Health 健康

隨著季節變遷,我們經常容易感到疲倦,如果你開始覺得有點身體不適,可要好好照顧自己。

開始多吃一些維他命 C,以增強抵抗力,就算真的感冒了,你也很快就能復原。

有些人相信增加體重就不容易生病。然而,醫生表示這並不可信。如果你多作休息並大量補充水分,幾天後情況仍然沒有好轉,就要請醫生來。別在身體虛弱的情況下出門,否則可能會昏倒。

Answer Key 解答

一、1. (D) 2. (D) 3. (D) 4. (A)

二、1. caught cold 2. got over 3. put on weight

三、1. I used to get sick when I was child, but I have learned to take care of my body.

2. I think we should send for a doctor.

3. I played basketball so hard one day that I almost passed out.

Lesson 8: Explanation 解釋說明

根據《度假：家庭假日旅遊指南》一書指出，家庭一起出遊佔了全美度假人數的百分之四十六。

至於其他的百分之五十四，假期研究員指出那幾乎包含了所有其他的人。休伯·辛格斯金表示：「假日很適合作家庭溝通，舉例來說，許多家長發現在森林裡比在客廳裡更容易與青少年溝通瞭解。」

就親子時間而言，在森林裡你有的是時間。

相對而言，你的孩子也很有可能不領情。青少年不想從購物中心中被拖走，更不用說是舒適的家了。

Answer Key 解答

一、1. (A) 2. (D) 3. (A) 4. (C)

二、1. pointed out 2. get / through to 3. let alone

三、1. I always wanted to follow my parents' suggestions; on the other hand, I wanted to pursue my dreams, too.

   2. I want you to tell me nothing but the truth.

   3. In terms of money and fame, becoming a doctor can be the best choice.

Translation 中文翻譯

Lesson 9: Advice 建議

就像天下的父親一樣，我對我兒子也有所期待，這些期望是否能成真或是落空都取決於他自己。

我父親教導我職場倫理與品性操守，我相信即使到了今天也依然適用。

現在時代當然不同了，但假如你能不被那許許多多負面的事物所打敗，並且沒把事情給搞砸，父母對你的期望就不算白費。

你的未來瀕臨危險。就像我對我兒子說的，要實現你的夢想，不要放棄。我對你的期望是：自我實現，永不屈服。

你要做得和我所認知的一樣好，甚至比自己認為可能做到的還要好。

Answer Key 解答

一、1. (C)　2. (A)　3. (A)　4. (B)

二、1. in vain　2. at stake　3. carry out

三、1. Try not to give in to pressure from your friends to start smoking.

2. You should never give up when things become difficult.

3. Criticism can help if you don't let it get the better of you.

Lesson 10: Time 時間

那麼你將搬離父母的家。

從現在起，由你來負責。你剛花了一整天的時間把東西搬進新家，到目前為止，你的新家看起來還不錯，你朋友們有說要來幫忙，但他們從沒準時過。

Translation 中文翻譯

你的新公寓雖然目前是乾淨的，但你馬上就會發現它不會永遠保持乾淨，你不想浪費時間日復一日地打掃，但現在不會有人跟在你後面幫你收拾。

等一下，這是你的房子，所以規則由你訂！如果你不想打掃，那就不必掃！

當你真要搬出去住，你會知道何時該搬。但也別急著獨立，慢慢來，把事情做好。

Answer Key 解答

一、1. (A) 2. (D) 3. (B) 4. (C)

二、1. for the time being 2. right away/answer 3. for good

三、1. It's a silly movie, so don't waste your time watching it.

2. Day after day, he gets up early to deliver the morning newspaper.

3. It's best to take your time and do your homework right.

Lesson 11: Frequency 頻率

我小時候，只想快快長大；一旦清楚自己已長大成人，反而希望自己仍是個小孩。

偶而我會回想過去那段純真、無憂無慮的日子，有時我倒希望自己有不同的作為，但我一直都知道，只要我全力以赴，盡其所能去學習，我和所有其他孩子一樣都有機會。

如今，破天荒地，我承認自己再也不會是十三歲的事實。我母親依然不時把我當作小孩子看待，我也一再地告訴她我已不是小孩子了。儘管很罕見，但我內心偷偷期望自己仍然是那個長不大的小孩。

Translation 中文翻譯

Answer Key 解答

一、1. (C) 2. (A) 3. (B) 4. (C)

二、1. Off and on 2. Every other 3. Once in a blue moon

三、1. She was a good student, but she knew she didn't stand a chance of getting into Harvard University.

2. Time and again, she tried to lose weight, but she couldn't stop eating donuts!

3. Hey, for once, I got an A+ on my test!

Lesson 12: Order 順序

每個人總會碰上麻煩，但對查德來說，麻煩似乎一個接一個排隊等著他。我們經常輪流騎我的摩托車上學，我們輪流穿戴黑色皮衣、手套以及機車安全帽，有一天，這一切給搞亂了。

這天輪到查德騎車，正當我要上巴士的時候，突然間，查德從街角呼嘯而來，起初我還以為他在玩，但不久我就發現不太對勁，有兩輛警車也快速彎過街角緊跟在他後面。

查德闖了紅燈，警察把他當成是飆車族，經過一段時間最後事情才弄清楚。長遠來看，我想他還是少碰摩托車為妙。

Answer Key 解答

一、1. (D) 2. (A) 3. (B) 4. (A)

二、1. about to 2. before long 3. at first

一式搞定狄克生片語　Translation 中文翻譯

三、1. I was walking in the park yesterday when all of a sudden, it began to rain.

2. We waited 20 minutes in the rain, but at last the bus arrived.

3. Working hard in college, now, will help you find a better job in the long run.

Lesson 13: Cause & Effect　因果關係

近來大家都<u>要</u>可愛的東西。

<u>因此</u>，許多速食餐廳和便利商店紛紛<u>推出</u>可愛的小貓、小狗玩偶，或者是任何<u>與</u>當紅電影或卡通裡<u>相關</u>的可愛動物。

<u>既然</u>這種現象已經發生，<u>導致</u>許多中學生要求更多可愛的玩意兒，<u>事實上</u>，許多孩子瘋狂收集這些可愛的玩具，而且還會把它們掛在書包上或別在衣服上。

每次只要有<u>舉辦</u>新的促銷活動，人們會花數小時排隊，等著拿到最新、最可愛的玩偶，有時候還會因為有人插隊而<u>爆發</u>爭吵。

我父母不讓我做這種事，當大家在排隊時，我都在唸書，<u>難怪</u>我的考試成績總是班上最好的。

Answer Key 解答

一、1. (A) 2. (D) 3. (C) 4. (A)

二、1. Now that 2. led to 3. No wonder

三、1. Do you know when next year Madonna's concert in London takes place?

2. I watched a fight between two of my friends break out in school yesterday.

3. I don't know him; in fact, I just met him tonight for the first time.

Lesson 14: Wealth 財富

有錢真好！

如果你有錢，你可以買任何想要的東西，什麼東西都很便宜。當別人努力省吃儉用存錢時，你可以盡情享受，做任何想做的事。

你可以整天睡覺，整晚血拼，你可以買下所有喜歡的東西：香水、當紅名牌、時髦名車……說都說不完。你可能買的東西太多了，商店老闆都要抱怨所有流行的貨品都賣光了。

當你生活富裕時，你不必去想如何賺錢謀生，因為你唯一的職責就是讓自己變得越來越有錢。當別人試圖擺脫沈重負債時，你可以坐在游泳池邊，花一整天想像你可以買些什麼。

錯了，你知道嗎？我實在不認為有錢可以讓你生活變得更好，錢買不到滿足感以及家人和朋友的愛。

即使用全世界的金子我也不願交換我的人生，在我內心裡我已經很富有了。

Answer Key 解答

一、1. (C)　2. (A)　3. (B)　4. (C)

二、1. trade / in / lemon　2. well-off / retire　3. earn a living

三、1. You must get out from under heavy debt if you want to be successful in life.

Translation 中文翻譯

2. You would be better off in school if you studied more and played less.

3. The most popular computer games are always sold out first.

Lesson 15: Contacting 接洽聯絡

當業務真難。

我總是忙著與人談話，我如果不是在作簡報，就是跟同事在討論新點子。

每天我都要聯絡新客戶，有時他們對我並不友善。我打電話給他們，告知我們公司有趣的新產品，我話都還沒說完，他們就掛電話。或者可能當我還在講，他們就要我稍候，結果再也沒回來接電話。

當我與他們會面，討論我們公司絕妙的服務時，他們會插話，要求我降價。順道一提，這可是假設我有辦法見到他們的情況。有好幾次他們說要跟我見面，但卻暫不確定日期，根本永遠也不會確定。

所以下次你跟業務人員交談時，請稍微站在我的立場想一想。

Answer Key 解答

一、1. (A) 2. (D) 3. (B) 4. (D)

二、1. talk over 2. By the way 3. leave the date open

三、1. People often hang up on salesmen when they call them at home.

Translation 中文翻譯

2. Sometimes small children will tell a caller to hold on, then forget to tell an adult someone is on the phone.

3. If you get lonely, just call me up and I'll come over.

Lesson 16: Argument 爭執

我通常不會說我朋友壞話，但前幾天布萊恩實在讓我生氣。

他要求我幫他寫學期報告。我告訴他放我一馬，我自己的都還沒寫好。他有點生氣，喔好吧，我不拐彎抹角，他簡直氣炸了，我只好跟他說我會幫他寫。

你有聽過朋友這麼做的嗎？我不喜歡挑人家毛病，但我開始覺得他在利用我。我跟他說我要打退堂鼓，但他說如果我不幫，他就去跟學校教務長告我的狀。搞得好像整件事是我引起的一樣。

我去找教務長把事情釐清。教務長因為我有涉入而斥責我。還有，現在我因為和他頂嘴而惹上麻煩！我不知道啦，但我想布萊恩也總得去找教務長吧！

Answer Key 解答

一、1. (A) 2. (D) 3. (B) 4. (C)

二、1. find fault with 2. back out 3. clear things up

三、1. Tony got into trouble at school and was called down by his teacher.

2. As children, it's really rude to talk back to adults, especially your parents.

3. Search me, I can't imagine where you might have put your keys this morning.

Translation 中文翻譯

Lesson 17: On the Job 工作

幾週前泰瑞問我是否可暫代他的工作，好讓他可以去海邊。我根本不適合做粗活，但我卻跟他說我會代他的班。他說園藝真的很簡單，我可以接替他的工作，不會有問題的。

通常這時候他會播新草種，但他說我可以不用管，只要繼續除草就好了。

我早上六點抵達第一個園藝場，完全準備好開始我的新工作。我裝設好除草機和其他設備。當我啟動電動除草機，園主跑出來對我大叫，說他無法忍受早上六點被吵醒。他說要把我解雇直到泰瑞回來工作為止。我第一天就被炒魷魚！

我很沮喪，所以就結束當天的工作去海邊找泰瑞。

Answer Key 解答

一、1. (A) 2. (B) 3. (A) 4. (B)

二、1. stand for 2. laid off 3. set up

三、1. I didn't do my homework, but the teacher let it slide this time.

2. Even though I finished my homework, I carried on reading all night.

3. It's time to call it a day.

Translation 中文翻譯

Lesson 18: Situations 狀況

我最喜歡做的事情之一是在我家附近當褓母。大體上,除了在那裡陪小孩外,沒什麼事要做。然而,遲早必定會有事情發生。

我男朋友來和我一起看書那次就很明顯。

我能找到這麼好的保姆工作,要歸功於我媽的朋友,對我來說情況逐漸好轉。那是間很大的豪宅,總之,孩子們都很乖。

一如往常,我準時到了那裡。當我正用手機在找我男朋友的電話號碼時,突然間,他敲了門。我有點被嚇到,並很快地轉身,差點就把桌上那只貴重的花瓶給打破。真的是千鈞一髮。那實在忍無可忍,從那時起,我帶小孩時就只以電視機為伴。

Answer Key 解答

一、1. (C) 2. (A) 3. (B) 4. (D)

二、1. turn around 2. thanks to 3. in all

三、1. If you want to be successful, you have to stand out from the crowd.
    2. Tony was late for class, as usual.
    3. Things are looking up for Taiwan.

Lesson 19: Extent 程度

我在唸書時,流傳著一個謠言,任何人想要演電影,只需去某片場,就至少能獲得一次試演的機會。

一式搞定狄克生片語 | Translation 中文翻譯

我想試試看。我根本不是演員,事實上,我完全沒有演過戲。我的朋友川特和我一道去,他可比我帥多了。

除了唸幾段臺詞外,我們還得打場撞球。我多少會打點撞球,但頂多稱得上一般水準。

川特與我合演一場打撞球起爭執的戲。這場戲很棒,但在我講完第二段台詞後,攝影機的底片就用完了。導演還是讓我們演完。

我的電影生涯總結而言,我想說雖然我不是電影明星,但我確實從中得到樂趣!

Answer Key 解答

一、1. (D) 2. (B) 3. (C) 4. (D)

二、1. by far 2. In addition to 3. more or less

三、1. Though I'm a very good writer, I'm an average public speaker at best.

2. The company may run out of money soon.

3. To sum up, I think that one's parents are the most important people in a person's life.

Lesson 20: Reactions 反應

你在學校可曾注意到那些耍酷的小孩似乎總是能為所欲為?

他們也就是那些瞧不起我們功課好的小孩。他們忘情於自己的酷炫模樣,而且又愛現,尤其是對他們的朋友。他們認為每個人都應該對他們奉承諂媚。

Translation 中文翻譯

我可不要再忍受這種情況！我要斷然地告訴他們我的感受。

別擔心，我不會生氣的，我會保持冷靜。

萬一他們找我麻煩時，你最好假裝不認識我！

Answer Key 解答

一、1. (A) 2. (D) 3. (C) 4. (A)

二、1. take it for granted 2. play up to 3. put up with

三、1. I want to make sure we solve this problem once and for all.

2. When you run into a dangerous situation, it is best to keep your head.

3. Making believe problems don't exist will not make them go away.

Lesson 21: Support 支持

我是那種當別人有需要就可能會來向我求助的人。我試著符合朋友對我的印象，沒什麼事會被完全排除。然而，對於某些事情我還是會予以拒絕。

當有人要求我幫忙時，無論如何，我盡量不回絕任何人的請求。你們最好祈求我永遠不會拒絕。我可能未必認同他們要我幫忙的事，但我相信他們所說：這事關重大，需要我幫忙。如果我不幫，誰會站出來幫他們呢？

這並不會讓我成為英雄，所以別為我掌聲鼓勵或頒獎牌給我。我不過是一個懂得關心且願意幫助人的人罷了。

Translation 中文翻譯

Answer Key 解答

一、1. (A) 2. (B) 3. (B) 4. (D)

二、1. turned me down 2. keep my / crossed 3. see eye to eye

三、1. If you believe in something, you should stand up for it.

2. It might sound negative, but I don't think you should take people at their word.

3. It was my first public performance the audience gave me a big hand.

Lesson 22: Relationships 關係

當你和某人從小一起長大，像我和布萊恩這樣，你們會發展出一種相互忍讓的關係。我們像兄妹般和睦相處。長大後，我們兩個都變了，他給我的印象比較像男友而非兄長。

我從未料到我會愛上他，但這卻發生了。我不曾透露我愛他有多深，我們剛上高中時便已固定交往。他過去常以我想像中男朋友應該有的方式照顧我，要是我們起爭執，他總是會道歉並和我重修舊好。

在我們高三的時候，他們全家搬走了，而我們必須分手，但我每個月仍會收到他的訊息，我知道有這麼一天他會停止鬼混，回到我身邊。

Answer Key 解答

一、1. (B) 2. (C) 3. (D) 4. (A)

二、1. let on 2. take care of 3. made up

Translation 中文翻譯

三、1. I had to break off with my boyfriend to go abroad to study.

2. After I left Canada, I never heard from Susan again.

3. Stop fooling around! It's time to get serious.

Lesson 23: Making Arrangements 安排

我朋友們和我都很喜歡露營。當我們開始計畫一趟露營行程時,我們會仔細考慮想要去哪裡,還有那次旅行我們想去哪種地形露營。

我們會考量時節、想從事什麼活動,以及要走的距離。我們不排除任何地方,因為如果我們有事先規劃,我們幾乎任何我們想去的地方都可預約到。

傑克是我們這群人的領隊,他很能幹。我們會把想法告訴他,萬一他不知道這個地方,他也有認識的人會知道。

果不其然,他總是有辦法幫我們在露營地找到最佳的地點。

Answer Key 解答

一、1. (B) 2. (C) 3. (D) 4. (B)

二、1. have in mind 2. feel like 3. in case

三、1. To get reservations at this hotel, you have to call a month in advance.

2. The manager took care of the problem immediately; she was really on the ball.

3. I didn't spend time preparing for my exams, so it figures that I didn't do well.

Lesson 24: Movement 動作

我自上次騎馬至今已經好多年了,不過戴爾堅持要我跟他一起去騎。我知道他喜歡騎很快,所以想在途中能趕上他,我驅車前往鄉下租匹馬先來趟試騎。

我所試的第一匹馬不肯高抬貴腳──或該說「貴蹄」。我挑的第二匹馬比較有朝氣,因此我握住韁繩,但牠只會在柵門及草地圍場之間來回踱步。

牧工牽出第三匹馬,他說:「我希望牠不會與你作對,我們叫牠『魔鬼』。」我要牛仔留下來看看所謂真正的騎士!「魔鬼」保持靜止沒多久,一分鐘後我就飛到空中,砰一聲摔到地上,然後頭昏眼花站起來說:「魔鬼真有朝氣!」

Answer Key 解答

一、1. (C) 2. (D) 3. (B) 4. (A)

二、1. stick around 2. rose to its feet 3. turn on

三、1. Before the race, I took hold of the wheel and got ready go.

   2. I couldn't hold myself still when the doctor wanted to give me a shot.

   3. The wolves didn't attack; they just paced back and forth, watching us.

Lesson 25: Obstacles 障礙

我是一位土木工程師，大學畢業後，我回到故鄉要讓鄉親們的生活變得更舒適。

我的家鄉是個小地方，運輸系統十分不方便。許多鐵路、交通號誌和路標都故障了。我想把這些都撤掉並更換系統，因為這造成阻礙，讓人們無法準時上班、準時回家。若非這樣的城鎮規劃，人們便可以多花點時間與家人相處。

我和鎮上官員們仔細討論過我所有的新計畫，他們很喜歡。但要改變談何容易，當我們開始動工，事情就出錯了。每次我去視察進度，總是會有工地的工作人員作阻撓。當然，施工人員也會認為我是在妨礙他們。我們無法達成共識。

然而，到了最後，我學到最好不要招惹是非，就和人們進行溝通。這很辛苦，但現在我的家鄉成了國內最安全便利的小鎮之一。

Answer Key 解答

一、1. (C) 2. (A) 3. (B) 4. (B)

二、1. went wrong 2. prevented / from 3. check up on

三、1. My parents told me that they would never interfere with my dreams and plans for my future.
  2. Don't make waves with your parents; just do what they say.
  3. I don't like people to get in my way when I'm trying to do something.

Lesson 26: Pay Attention 警覺

在學校當導護人員可不容易。你得隨時提高警覺留意匆忙又不注意規則的小孩。

要留意所有雙向奔跑、想在時間結束前穿越馬路的那些小朋友，可能會有困難。

Translation 中文翻譯

還有許多其他事情可能會發生，讓你措手不及。如果你不密切注意孩子們，他們可能會迷路。

有時你必須協助孩子尋找他們的父母。你必須留心突然開到街上來的汽機車。這實在是壓力沈重而且責任重大。

我先生一直跟我說我應該好好考慮找個新工作，但我絕對不會換工作的。

Answer Key 解答

一、1. (A) 2. (B) 3. (B) 4. (D)

二、1. keep track of 2. turned up 3. see about

三、1. I would like to look for a job that uses my math and science skills.
  2. My parents taught me to look out for people who might try to take advantage of me.
  3. I didn't know you were going to throw me a party; it took me by surprise.

Lesson 27: Differences 判別

當我移居國外念書時，我發現在另一個國家生活和國內大為不同。首先，我老是會迷路，路標看起來都一樣！我很快就認得我周遭的環境，這是我唯一能夠找到宿舍的方法。總之我不善於辨認方向，我想這方面和我父親很像。

還有，老實說，我一看到那裡的食物就覺得有點反胃。但我盡量試著少吃自己國家的食物，我想體驗我新家當地人民的生活。

Translation 中文翻譯

第一天我到辦公室去查看我在課程上所作的一些變更，在辦公室裡我無法辨別誰是誰。一位和善的女士檢視我的資料後就離開了。辦公室裡另一位小姐過來問我一個問題，我卻將她誤認成第一位女士。真的是很糗。

Answer Key 解答

一、1. (A) 2. (C) 3. (D) 4. (A)

二、1. took her for 2. cut down on 3. look into

三、1. These two boxes are so alike, I couldn't tell them apart.
   或 These two boxes are so alike, I couldn't tell one from the other.

   2. When I was a child I always used to ask my father to look over my homework.

   3. I could never be a doctor because I get faint at the sight of blood.

Lesson 28: In Charge 管控

我高中最好的朋友巴德和我決定利用網路開創自己的事業。我們其實並不知道自己在做什麼，但我們知道如果我們能夠隨機應變，幾乎任何事我們都可以成功過關。

我們開始我們的電腦維修事業，我負責辦公室事務。我知道我可以仰賴巴德做維修工作，因為他總是不辭辛勞跟上最新科技的腳步。

我想要擁有漂亮的辦公室，但我們得將就使用一個便宜的店面。巴德想要一個很棒的實驗室，所以我們就折中讓他有一個工作台。

我們想建議所有想自己當老闆的人，還是開始培養個嗜好吧！因為在真實世界裡，不是所有你認為在掌控之中的事都真的是在掌握中！

275

Translation 中文翻譯

Answer Key 解答

一、1. (B) 2. (D) 3. (A) 4. (D)

二、1. meet me halfway 2. takes pains 3. in hand

三、1. You always keep your promises, so I know I can count on you.

2. My father retired and decided to take up fishing as a new hobby.

3. I really want a BMW, but I'll have to make do with a Ford because it's less expensive.

Lesson 29: Scheduling 時程

在旺季期間我們工作進度總是落後。訣竅是要逐漸趕上進度。如果不這樣，就毫無希望趕上。

為了要趕上進度，我們只好將就不放假。我老闆說他還想要取消午餐時間，但我說，我認為最好還是延後再作決定。

如果我們可以及時開始進行專案以趕上截止期限，並持續按照進度進行，我們還是有機會準時完成。

一旦完成，我們有時會想延長交貨期，這樣其他潛在客戶就能看到我們製作的品質。

Answer Key 解答

一、1. (B) 2. (A) 3. (C) 4. (D)

二、1. do without 2. little by little 3. catch up on

三、1. The teacher will hold over the test until Monday.
   或 The teacher will put off the test until Monday.

   2. If you don't get up in time, you'll be late for school.

   3. We were able to stay on schedule.

Lesson 30: Crimes 犯罪

史帝夫在一家便利商店工作。他說了這個故事，有一晚上夜班時，一個傢伙帶了把槍進來搶劫商店。這名搶匪試圖撬開保險箱，但卻打不開，所以他就要把它炸開。史帝夫想那可能會讓大樓著火，而且可能會整棟燒毀，於是他告訴他保險箱才剛被清空。

那傢伙放掉他的槍，當槍撞到地板時，走火射到櫃檯上的一盒打火機。打火機著了火，而旁邊的一堆爆米花也開始爆開。那個傢伙試著撕開他的襯衫用來將火熄滅，但並不管用。他開始道歉，甚至問急救箱在哪裡。

所以我們實在不能說是因警方取締才讓這起搶案未能得逞。據說他可能是想報復老闆，其實並不想傷害任何人。

Answer Key 解答

一、1. (A) 2. (B) 3. (D) 4. (C)

二、1. tore up 2. burned down 3. put out

三、1. If someone hurts you, it's natural to want to get even with them.

   2. The police put down the riot in a short time.

   3. The child refused to let go of his candy.

Appendix 附錄

本附錄將新、舊版狄克生片語彙整分為三十大主題，並依照各主題之英文字母順序排列，以方便讀者參照、查詢，希望能幫助讀者將所有片語串連起來，以增進學習效果。

Advice 建議

at stake 瀕臨危險
carry out 執行；實現
come true 成真；實現
fall through 失敗；落空
follow in one's footsteps 效法；繼承衣缽
get the better of 打敗；勝過
give in 屈服；投降
give up 放棄；戒除
give way to 讓步；屈服
goof up 搞砸
hold good 仍有效；仍適用
in vain 徒勞無功
knock out 擊倒；強烈吸引
land on one's feet 重新站起來
miss the boat 錯過機會
pull off 成功做到；靠邊停車
put one's foot in it 搞砸
screw up 搞砸
stick to 堅持
to good purpose 很有成效
touch and go 不到最後沒有定論

Argument 爭執

back out 退出；食言
be had 被騙
beat around the bush 拐彎抹角
call down 責備
clear up 澄清；清理
convince of 說服；使信服
find fault with 挑毛病；找碴
get stuck 被騙
give (someone) a break 放⋯⋯一馬；饒了⋯⋯吧
have a voice in 在⋯⋯有發言權
hear of 聽說；得知
hold one's tongue 緘默
in public 當眾地；公開地
keep after 不斷嘮叨、提醒
leave alone 不打擾；保持距離
search me 我不知道；問倒我
shut up 閉嘴
speak ill of 說人壞話
speak one's mind 說內心話
stick it to 欺騙
talk back to 頂嘴
think of 覺得；認為
waste one's breath 徒費唇舌

Cause and Effect 因果關係

as a matter of fact 事實上
as a result 結果；因此
ask for 要求；活該
break out 爆發；發生
bring about 引起；造成
by dint of 由於；憑藉
by means of 由於；憑藉
come about 發生
have to do with 與⋯⋯有關
in consequence 因此
in consequence of 結果
in fact 事實上；其實
in the name of 為了；依⋯⋯的名義
lead to 導致；通往
no wonder 難怪
now that 既然；因為
owe to 受惠於；歸功於
owing to 因為；由於
result from 因⋯⋯所造成
result in 導致
serve (someone) right 活該；罪有應得

take place 舉行；發生
turn into 變成
turn out 結果變成；出席

Contacting 接洽聯絡

be in (someone's) shoes 站在某人的立場
break in 逐漸用慣；插話
by the way 順便一提
call up 打電話
cut in 插嘴；插隊
drop a line 寫張便條
face-to-face 面對面地
get in touch with 與……聯絡
give someone a ring 打電話給某人
hang up 掛斷電話；懸掛
hold on 稍候；抓緊；堅持
in contact with 接觸；會面
in touch 聯絡
keep in touch with 保持聯絡
kick around （非正式）討論
leave open 暫緩決定
out of touch 沒聯絡；搞不清楚
ring up 打電話
take up with 與……商量
talk over 討論；商量
throw a curve 提出意想不到的話題

Crimes 犯罪

blow away 吹走
blow down 吹落
blow off 吹倒
blow out 破裂；吹熄
blow up 爆炸
break into 闖入；侵入
break through 打破；突破
break up 打碎
burn down 燒毀
burn out 燒壞；筋疲力竭

burn up 燒毀；燒掉
catch fire 著火
chop up 砍碎；剁碎
cut off 切掉；中斷
cut out 剪下；中止
cut up 切碎
get even with 報復
go off 爆炸；響起
hold up 持槍搶劫
lay hands on 逮捕
let go (of) 放開；釋放
make away with 殺；毀棄
put down 放下；鎮壓
put out 熄滅；使不省人事
put to death 處死
round up 趕攏；逮捕
set fire to 放火；焚燒
set on fire 放火
tear down 拆毀；扯下
tear off 扯掉
tear up 撕裂；撕毀
throw the book at 嚴厲懲罰

Differences 判別

all the same 完全一樣；儘管如此
at the sight of 一看見……就
be a far cry from 與……大為不同
cut down on 減少；削減
cut short 剪短；中止
die away 逐漸消失
die down 減弱
die out 滅絕；過時
fade away 逐漸消失
first-rate 一流的；卓越的
know by sight 認得；見過面
leave out 刪除
let up 逐漸減弱
look into 調查
look over 檢視；過目

make a difference 很重要；有影響
make no difference 沒有區別
mistake for 誤認
stick up 凸出來；行竊
take after 與……相像
take for 將……視為；將……誤認為
tell from 辨別
upside down 上下顛倒

Dressing 服飾穿著

be in/out 流行／過時
catch on 形成風潮；聽懂
dress up 盛裝打扮
have on 穿著
inside out 內外反過來
let out 放大尺寸
make over 翻新；改造
out of date 舊式的；落伍的
pick out 挑選
put on 穿戴
take in 拜訪；縮小尺寸
take off 脫掉；起飛
throw away 丟掉
try on 試穿
up to date 現在的；最新的
wear away/down 磨損；磨破
wear off 逐漸消失
wear out 穿壞；磨損
wear through 磨破；穿破

Driving 開車

back up 倒車；向後退
drive up to 開往；駛近
drop off 中途下車
dry up 乾涸
en route 在途中
get in 搭乘汽車
get lost 迷路

get off 下車
get on 上車
get out of 下車
get wet 弄濕
hold up 延遲
make room for 讓位；騰出空間
rain cats and dogs 傾盆大雨
run into 撞上
run over 輾過
slow down 放慢速度
slow up 減低速度
walk up to 走到

Eating 飲食

bite off 咬斷
chew off 嚼斷
chew up 咬碎
clean up 洗手（臉）
dish out 分裝；辱罵
eat in/out 在家吃／吃餐館
eat up 吃完；吃掉
go Dutch 各自付帳
help yourself 自行取用
pick up the tab 付帳
sit down 坐下
taste of 嚐起來有……的味道
throw up 嘔吐
wait on 服務；接待

Explanation 解釋說明

above all 尤其；特別是
according to 根據；遵照
account for 佔了……；說明
and what not 等等
as for 至於；關於
as to 關於
at heart 其實；根本上
for all 雖然；不管

for example 例如
get off one's chest 表白；開誠佈公
get through to 使瞭解；聯絡上
in effect 事實上
in one's opinion 依據……的意見
in particular 尤其；特別地
in terms of 就……而言
let alone 更不必說
make clear 說清楚講明白
no matter 不論
no other than 就是
nothing but 只是；只不過
nothing else than 不過是；不外是
on the other hand 另一方面
point out 指出
stand to reason 合乎道理
take shape 具體化；成形
with reference to 關於；有關

Extent 程度

at all 一點也；到底
at best 充其量；頂多
at least 至少
by far 遠高於；顯著地
by no means 絕不；一點也不
fifty-fifty 一半一半；等分
go around 散播；足夠分配
in a lump 總計；全部
in addition to 除……之外
in proportion to 按著……的比例
in the worst way 非常；很
more or less 或多或少；差不多
not a whit 一點也不
quite a few 相當多的
run out of 用完
sum up 總計；作總結
ten to one 十之八九
to a degree 非常

Family Life 居家生活

answer the door 應門
be used to 已習慣……
bring up 撫養
call on 要求；拜訪
clean off 使整潔
clean out 清潔；整理
clean up 清潔；打掃
come from 來自
drop in on （短暫）拜訪
get into the habit of 養成……習慣
get up 起床
get used to 適應；習慣於
give birth to 生產
go to bed 上床睡覺
grow out of 因長大而脫離
keep house 管理家務
keep up 無法入睡；保持
make up 化妝
name after 以……命名
put away 處理；收拾
run away 離家出走；私奔
see off 送行
stay in/out 留在家／不在家
stop by 暫停；稍事停留
take leave of 辭行；告別
wait up for 不睡覺等著
wake up 醒來

Frequency 頻率

all along 一直；一開始就
as soon as 一……立刻……
at times 有時；偶而
every now and then 有時；偶而
every other 每隔……的；所有其他的
every so often 偶爾
few and far between 極少；機會很低
for once 就這麼一次；僅此一次
in between whiles 一有空閒

now and then 偶爾
off and on 斷斷續續
once in a blue moon 很少；不常
once in a while 偶爾
over and over 一再
stand a chance 有希望；有可能
the minute/moment 一……就……
time and again 屢次；一再地

Health 健康

bring to 使……甦醒
build up 增進；增強
catch cold 著涼
come to 恢復意識
get over 復原
get sick 生病
get tired 疲倦
get well 康復
hard of hearing 聽力不好
look after 照顧；照料
pass out 昏倒；分發
put on weight 增加體重
send for 延請某人
tired out 非常疲倦
under the weather 身體不適

In Charge 管控

answer for 擔保；對…負責
at will 隨意；任意
be in charge of 管理；負責
bow out 引退；縮手作罷
break away 逃脫
break loose 脫逃
cop out 逃避責任；藉口
count on 依靠；仰賴
drop out of 退出；脫離
get away 逃離
get away with 成功過關；逃過懲罰
get out of line 不遵守規定

go for 努力爭取
go through channels 循正常管道
have charge of 掌管
in exchange for 以…為交換
in hand 在掌握之中
keep away (from) 遠離
keep off 遠離
keep out 不許進入
knock oneself out 卯足全力
make do 將就；權宜之計
make the best of 竭盡全力
make up one's mind 下決心
make use of 利用
meet (someone) halfway 妥協；讓步
never mind 不要緊
no party to 不參與
odds and ends 瑣碎之事物
on hand 在手邊；在附近
persist in 堅持
play by ear 憑印象演奏；見機行事
pull together 蒐集；冷靜下來
rely on 依靠；信賴
step in 介入；進去一下
take charge of 負責
take pains 不辭辛勞；費盡苦心
take up 開始；著手進行

Learning 學習

be over one's head 無法理解；十分忙碌
bear in mind 記得
brush up on 復習
by heart 記住
call the roll 點名
commit to memory 熟記
cross out 刪掉
figure out 想出；弄清楚
get along 有進步
glance over 瀏覽；簡略地讀
hand in 繳交
hold out 持續；抵抗支撐

learn the ropes 學會訣竅
look up 查閱;查詢
lose one's touch 變生疏
major in 主修
make out 做（得好）;瞭解
make up 補考
read over 從頭到尾讀一遍
stay up 熬夜
take down 取下;記下
try one's best 盡全力

Making Arrangement 安排

bring back 送還
bring out 推出;拿出來
do over 重做;重複
feel like 想要……
figure on 打算;指望
had better 最好
have got 有;持有
have in mind 想著;打算
in advance 事先;預先
in case 以防萬一;要是……的話
it figures 似乎有理;果不其然
keep in mind 考慮;想著
make sense 有道理;有意義
on the ball 機警;能幹
rule out 排除;不予考慮
set out to 開始做;打算
take into account 加以考慮
think over 仔細考慮
think up 想出;突發奇想

Movement 動作

back and forth 來回地;前後地
by oneself 單獨
dry run 排練;預演
fall off 跌下;落下;減少
get back 返回

get to 可以做;到達
give off 發出
go out 離開;熄滅
go up to 接近;前往
high and low 到處
hold still 保持靜止
in person 親自
keep up with 趕上;並駕齊驅
lie down 躺下
liven up 使活躍
make good time 快速前進
make the round of 繞行;兜圈子
on foot 步行;徒步
pick up 拾起;購買;搭載
right here 就在這裡
right there 就在那裡
rise to one's feet 站起來
run up to 跑到
show up 出現
sit down 坐下
stand up 起立;耐用
stick around 待在這裡等
stick out 伸直;突出
take a seat 坐下
take hold of 握住;抓住
take out 取出
tie up 捆好
to and fro 來回地
turn off 關閉
turn on 與……敵對;打開
wind up 上發條

Obstacles 阻礙

be in the/one's way 造成阻礙
be the matter 怎麼了;出狀況
break down 故障;擊倒
but for 若非
check on 調查
check up on 調查;檢查

dry out 使變乾；戒除酒癮
get rid of 去除；擺脫
go over 仔細檢查、審查
go wrong 出差錯；發生故障
interfere with 妨礙
kick the habit 戒掉壞習慣
make waves 引起騷動；惹是生非
nothing the matter 沒問題；沒毛病
of consequence 重要的
out of order 雜亂無章；故障
pin on 讓某人背黑鍋
prevent from 阻礙；防止
shut off 關閉
think a lot of 看重；重視
throw away 廢棄
throw out 丟棄；駁回

On the Job 工作

be cut out for 很適合；能勝任
be up for grabs 可得的；供爭奪的
buy out 收購；買進
call it a day 結束當天的工作
carry on 繼續
cover for 暫代；掩護
draw up 起草
fill in 填寫；告知
fill out 填寫
give out 分發；用完
go up 上漲；拉抬
lay off 解雇；裁員
let slide 丟著不管；怠忽職守
mind the store 看店
on duty 值班；執勤
on leave 請假
put together 裝配；組裝
put up 建造
see out 送到外面
set down 記載；放下
set up 設立；裝設（機器等）
shake hands 握手

stand for 代表；忍受
stand on ceremony 拘禮
step down 下台
take advantage of 利用；佔便宜
take apart 拆卸
take on 雇用；承擔
take over 接管；接替
try out 試用
turn over 移交

Order 順序

about to 即將；正要
all of a sudden 突然
at first 起初
at last 最後；終於
before long 很快；不久
by turns 輪流；輪替地
get mixed up 搞混
in the long run 終究；到最後
in turn 輪流；依次地
mix up 搞混；充分混合
one after another 一個接一個
sooner or later 遲早
take turns 輪流
wait for 等候

Paying Attention 警覺

beware of 當心；注意
conscious of 察覺到；意識到
find out 得知
in a hurry 匆忙地；急忙地
in existence 存在；現在的
in search of 尋找
keep an eye on 留意
keep track of 追蹤；密切注意
look at 注視
look for 尋找
look on 觀賞；觀看

look out 小心；留心
look out on 面對；瞭望
on one's toes 提高警覺的；準備好的
pay attention (to) 注意；專心
see about 留意；安排
take a look at 看看
take by surprise 出其不意；使……驚訝
to one's face 當面
turn up 出現；增強
watch out for 留意

Reactions 反應

be up to 全看……；正在做……
broad-minded 心胸寬大
change one's mind 改變心意
feel sorry for 為……惋惜
get a rise out of 嘲笑而惹火某人
get carried away 忘情於；不能自己
get cold feet 怯懦；膽怯
get on one's nerve 令人心煩
go off the deep end 勃然大怒
have it in for 懷恨在心
have one's way 照某人的意思去做
ill at ease 忐忑不安
keep one's head 保持冷靜
look down on 瞧不起；輕視
look up to 尊敬；仰望
lose one's cool 失去冷靜
lose one's head 驚慌失措
lose one's temper 發脾氣
make believe 假裝
mourn for/over 悲悼；哀弔
narrow-minded 心胸狹窄
of oneself 自動地
on edge 緊張；焦慮
on purpose 故意
once and for all 僅此一次；斷然地
play up to 討好
put on airs 裝腔作勢；擺架子
put up with 忍受

show off 賣弄；炫耀
step on 嚴厲對待；快一點
stir up 激起
take for granted 視為理所當然
take pity on 同情
take pleasure in 引以為榮
would rather 寧願

Relationships 關係

break off 斷絕；分手
come across 不期而遇
confide to 吐露（祕密等）
confidence in 有信心；相信
fall for 迷戀；被騙
fall in love 戀愛
fix up 安排；解決
fool around 鬼混；胡鬧
get along with 相處融洽
give and take 相互忍讓；彼此妥協
go with 與……交往；搭配
have it out with 與……吵架；對立
hear from 得到某人的音訊
in honor of 為祝賀；為紀念……
indulge in 耽溺；縱情
let on 洩露；透露
make faces 扮鬼臉
make friends 交朋友
make fun of 嘲笑
make up 補償；和解
make up with 重修舊好
paly jokes on 跟……開玩笑
paly tricks on 跟……開玩笑
run across 不期而遇
run into 不期而遇；撞上
take back 送還
take care of 照顧；處理
take to 喜歡；耽於
turn to 求助於

Scheduling 時程

a lost cause 毫無希望
all at once 突然
all of a sudden 突然
be over 結束
be with it 提起幹勁
burst out 突然開始；衝出去
by chance 偶然；意外
call off 取消
catch up 趕上；追上
come to an end 終結
do away with 廢除；除去；擺脫
do without 沒有……也行；沒有……而將就
end off 結束
fall behind 落後
gather oneself (together) 打起精神
get busy 忙碌
get through 完成
go through 經歷；用完；通過
hold off 延遲
hold over 延長；延期
in time 及時；來得及
in time to 趕上做……
keep on 繼續
lag behind 落後
little by little 逐漸地
lose heart 氣餒
make good 進行順利
on schedule 按照預定時間；準時
put an end to 終止
put off 拖延；延遲
take the bull by the horns 不畏艱難
with a will 熱心；努力

Situations 狀況

all in all 整體而言
as a rule 通常；大致
as if 似乎；好像
as usual 通常；一如往常

at random 胡亂地；隨便地
be bound to 一定會
be looking up 逐漸好轉；有起色
become of 變成
can not but 不得不
clear-cut 明確的；明快的
close call 千鈞一髮
cut and dried 明確的；無聊的
for certain 確實的；無疑的
for sure 確實的；無疑的
get better 好轉
get worse 惡化；變壞
go on 發生；繼續
have got to 必須
in a body 全體
last straw 達到容忍極限
on the whole 大體上；大致
serve the purpose 有用；符合
stand out 顯著；突出
thanks to 幸虧
turn around 轉身；逆轉

Support 支持

all right 對的
be with 支持；聽懂
by all means 無論如何；務必
call for 需要；強力主張
cheer up 鼓舞；使高興
draw the line at 拒絕；到此為止
give (someone) a big hand 為……掌聲鼓勵
give (someone) a hand 幫助
go without saying 不用說
have one's heart set on 渴望；下定決心
keep one's fingers crossed 祈求
keep one's word 守信
live up to 遵守；達到
make sure 確定
not on your life 絕不；想都別想
of course 當然
out of the question 不可能；門都沒有

see eye to eye 意見一致
stand up for 支持；維護
take at one's word 相信某人說的話
turn down 拒絕；減低
with one accord 一致地
without fail 務必；一定

Time 時間

all day long 整天
as yet 到目前為止
at once 立刻
be up 時間到了；結束
day after day 日復一日
day in and day out 天天；逐日
for good 永久；永遠
for the time being 目前；暫時
from now on 從現在起
in no time 立即；很快
keep good time 時間準確
of late 最近
on the instant 瞬間；剎那
on time 準時
right away 立刻；馬上
right now 即刻
so far 到目前為止
take one's time 別急；慢慢來
tell time 會看時間
waste time over 浪費時間
year after year 年復一年
year in and year out 年復一年

Trips 旅遊

check in/out 住／退房登記
go in for 愛好；熱衷
goof off 混日子；打混
have a good time 玩得愉快
line up 排隊
look forward to 期待；盼望

set forth 出發
set out 出發；開始
take a trip 旅行
take a walk 散步
take it easy 放鬆心情
take part (in) 參加
take time off 休假；休息
work out 健身；想出（計畫等）

Wealth 財富

a man of birth 出身高貴的人
a rainy day 窮困時
a steal 非常便宜
above one's fortune 付不起
be better off 情況好轉；更有錢
be well-off 生活富裕
buy up 全部買下；大量收購
cut corners 節省；偷工減料
earn a living 賺錢謀生
get out from under 擺脫負擔
in need 貧困；患難
live from hand to mouth 僅可糊口
live it up 盡情享樂；花費闊綽
raise money 集資
sell out 賣完；銷售一空
trade in 以舊品折價買新品
well-to-do 富裕的

Lesson 1 飲食 Eating

1. eat in/out 在家吃／吃餐館
2. wait on 服務；接待
3. dish out 分裝；辱罵
4. help yourself 自行取用
5. eat up 吃完；吃掉
6. taste of 嚐起來有……的味道
7. throw up 嘔吐
8. clean up 洗手（臉）
9. pick up the tab 付帳
10. go Dutch 各自付帳

Lesson 2 服飾穿著 Dressing

1. wear out 穿破；穿壞
2. dress up 盛裝打扮
3. inside out 內外反過來
4. up to date 最新的；現在的
5. take off 脫掉
6. try on 試穿
7. took in 縮小尺寸
8. pick out 挑選
9. put on 穿戴；塗抹
10. be in/out 流行／過時

Lesson 3 居家生活 Family Life

1. stay in/out 留在家／不在家
2. stop by 暫停；稍事停留
3. get used to 適應；習慣於
4. bring up 撫養
5. call on 要求；拜訪
6. clean out 清潔；整理
7. put away 處理；收拾
8. get up 起床
9. see off 送行
10. make up 化妝

Lesson 4 開車 Driving

1. get lost 迷路
2. drop off 中途下車
3. drive up to 開往；駛近
4. make room for 讓位；騰出空間
5. get in 搭乘汽車
6. back up 倒車；向後退
7. get on 上車
8. slow down 放慢速度
9. run over 輾過
10. run into 撞上

Lesson 5 旅遊 Trips

1. look forward to 期待；盼望
2. goof off 混日子；打混
3. set out 出發；開始
4. line up 排隊
5. check in/out 住／退房登記
6. take it easy 放鬆心情
7. work out 健身；想出（計畫等）
8. take time off 休假；休息
9. take part (in) 參加
10. having a good time 玩得愉快

Lesson 6 學習 Learning

1. major in 主修
2. stay up 熬夜
3. read over 從頭到尾讀一遍
4. by heart 記住
5. hand in 繳交
6. figure out 想出；弄清
7. learn the ropes 學會訣竅
8. call the roll 點名
9. look up 查閱；查詢
10. lose one's touch 變生疏

Lesson 7 健康 Health

1. get tired 疲倦
2. under the weather 身體不適
3. look after 照顧；照料
4. build up 增進；增強
5. catch cold 感冒
6. get over 復原
7. put on weight 增加體重
8. get sick 生病
9. send for 延請某人
10. pass out 昏倒；分發

Lesson 8 解釋說明 Explanation

1. according to 根據；遵照
2. account for 佔了……；說明
3. as for 至於；關於
4. point out 指出
5. for example 例如
6. get through to 使瞭解；聯絡上
7. in terms of 就……而言
8. nothing but 只是；只不過
9. on the other hand 另一方面
10. let alone 更不用說

Lesson 9 建議 Advice

1. come true 成真；實現
2. fall through 失敗；落空
3. hold good 仍有效；仍適用
4. get the better of 打敗；勝過
5. screw up 搞砸
6. in vain 徒勞無功
7. at stake 瀕臨危險
8. carry out 執行；實現
9. give up 放棄；戒除
10. give in 屈服；讓步

Lesson 10 時間 Time

1. from now on 從現在起
2. all day long 整天
3. so far 到目前為止
4. on time 準時
5. for the time being 目前；暫時
6. right away 立刻
7. for good 永久；永遠
8. waste time over 浪費時間
9. day after day 日復一日
10. take one's time 別急；慢慢來

Lesson 11 頻率 Frequency

1. as soon as 一……立刻……
2. at times 有時；偶而
3. every now and then 有時；偶而
4. all along 一直；從一開始就
5. stand a chance 有希望；有可能
6. every other 每隔……的；所有其他
7. for once 就這麼一次；僅此一次
8. off and on 斷斷續續
9. time and again 屢次；一再地
10. once in a blue moon 很少；不常

Lesson 12 順序 Order

1. sooner or later 遲早
2. one after another 一個接一個
3. take turns 輪流
4. mix up 搞混；充分混合
5. about to 即將；正要
6. all of a sudden 突然
7. at first 起初
8. before long 很快；不久
9. at last 最後；終於
10. in the long run 終究；到最後

Lesson 13 因果關係 Cause & Effect

1. ask for 要求；活該
2. as a result 結果；因此
3. turn out 結果變成；生產；出席
4. have to do with 與……有關
5. now that 既然；因為
6. lead to 導致；通往
7. in fact 事實上；其實
8. take place 舉行；發生
9. break out 爆發；發生
10. no wonder 難怪

Lesson 14 財富 Wealth

1. a steal 非常便宜
2. cut corners 節省；偷工減料
3. live it up 盡情享樂；花費闊綽
4. buy up 全部買下；大量收購
5. sell out 賣完；銷售一空
6. be well-off 生活富裕
7. earn a living 賺錢謀生
8. get out from under 擺脫負擔
9. be better off 情況好轉；更有錢
10. trade in 以舊品折價買新品

Lesson 15 接洽聯絡 Contacting

1. kick around （非正式）討論
2. get in touch with 與……聯絡
3. call up 打電話
4. hang up 掛斷電話；懸掛
5. hold on 稍候；抓緊；堅持
6. talk over 討論；商量
7. cut in 插嘴；插隊
8. by the way 順便一提
9. leave open 暫緩決定
10. be in (someone's) shoes 站在某人的立場

Lesson 16 爭執 Argument

1. speak ill of 說人壞話
2. give (someone) a break 放……一馬；饒了……吧
3. beat around the bush 拐彎抹角
4. hear of 聽說；得知
5. find fault with 挑毛病；找碴
6. back out 退出；食言
7. clear up 澄清；清理
8. call down 責罵
9. talk back to 頂嘴
10. search me 我不知道；問倒我

Lesson 17 工作 On the Job

1. cover for 暫代；掩護
2. be cut out for 很適合；能勝任
3. on duty 值班；執勤
4. take over 接管；接替
5. let slide 丟著不管；怠忽職守
6. carry on 繼續
7. set up 設立；裝設（機器等）
8. stand for 代表；忍受
9. lay off 解雇；裁員
10. call it a day 結束當天的工作

Lesson 18 狀況 Situations

1. on the whole 大體上；大致上
2. be bound to 一定會
3. stand out 顯著；突出
4. thanks to 幸虧
5. all in all 整體而言
6. as usual 通常；一如往常
7. be looking up 逐漸好轉；有起色
8. turn around 轉身；逆轉
9. close call 千鈞一髮
10. last straw 達到容忍極限

Lesson 19 程度 Extent

1. go around 散播；足夠分配
2. at least 至少
3. by no means 絕不；一點也不
4. at all 一點也；到底
5. by far 遠高於；顯著地
6. in addition to 除……之外
7. more or less 或多或少；差不多
8. at best 充其量；頂多
9. run out of 用完
10. sum up 總計；作總結

Lesson 20 反應 Reactions

1. have one's way 照某人的意思做
2. look down on 瞧不起；輕視
3. get carried away 忘情於；不能自己
4. show off 賣弄；炫耀
5. take for granted 視為理所當然
6. play up to 討好
7. put up with 忍受
8. once and for all 僅此一次；斷然地
9. keep one's head 保持冷靜
10. make believe 假裝

Lesson 21 支持 Support

1. live up to 遵守；達到
2. out of the question 不可能
3. draw the line at 拒絕；到此為止
4. by all means 無論如何；務必
5. turn down 拒絕；減低
6. keep one's fingers crossed 祈求
7. see eye to eye 意見一致
8. take at one's word 相信某人的話
9. stand up for 支持；維護
10. give (someone) a big hand 為……掌聲鼓勵

Lesson 22 關係 Relationships

1. give and take 相互忍讓；彼此妥協
2. get along with 相處融洽
3. come across 不期而遇；給予印象
4. fall for 迷戀；被騙
5. let on 洩露；透露
6. take care of 照顧；處理
7. make up with 重修舊好
8. break off 斷絕；分手
9. hear from 得到某人的音訊
10. fool around 鬼混；胡鬧

Lesson 23 安排 Making Arrangements

1. set out to 開始做；打算
2. think over 仔細考慮
3. take into account 加以考慮
4. rule out 排除；不予考慮
5. in advance 事先；預先
6. feel like 想要……
7. on the ball 機警；能幹
8. have in mind 想著；打算
9. in case 以防萬一；要是……的話
10. it figures 似乎有理；果不其然

Lesson 24 動作 Movement

1. keep up with 趕上；並駕齊驅
2. make good time 快速前進
3. dry run 排練；預演
4. pick up 拾起；購買；搭載
5. take hold of 握住；抓住
6. back and forth 來回地；前後地
7. turn on 與……敵對；打開
8. stick around 待在這裡等
9. hold still 保持靜止
10. rise to one's feet 站起來

Lesson 25 阻礙 Obstacles

1. out of order 雜亂無章；故障
2. get rid of 去除；擺脫
3. prevent from 阻礙；防止
4. but for 若非
5. go over 仔細檢查、審查
6. go wrong 出差錯；發生故障
7. check up on 調查；檢查
8. interfere with 阻礙；妨礙
9. be in the/one's way 造成阻礙
10. make waves 引起騷動；惹是生非

Lesson 26 警覺 Paying Attention

1. on one's toes 提高警覺的；準備好的
2. in a hurry 匆忙地；急忙地
3. pay attention (to) 注意；專心
4. keep an eye on 留意
5. turn up 增強；出現
6. take by surprise 出其不意
7. keep track of 追蹤；密切注意
8. look for 尋找
9. look out 小心；留心
10. see about 留意；安排

Lesson 27 判別 Differences

1. be a far cry from 與……大為不同
2. all the same 完全一樣；儘管如此
3. know by sight 認得；見過面
4. take after 與……相像
5. at the sight of 一看見……就
6. cut down on 減少；削減
7. look into 調查
8. tell from 辨別
9. look over 檢視；過目
10. take for 將……視為；將……誤認為

Lesson 28 管控 In Charge

1. make use of 利用
2. play by ear 憑印象演奏；見機行事
3. get away with 成功過關；逃過懲罰
4. be in charge of 管理；負責
5. count on 依靠；仰賴
6. take pains 不辭辛勞；費盡苦心
7. make do 將就；權宜之計
8. meet (someone) halfway 妥協
9. take up 開始；著手進行
10. in hand 在掌握之中

Lesson 29 時程 Scheduling

1. fall behind 落後
2. catch up 趕上；追上
3. little by little 逐漸地
4. a lost cause 毫無希望
5. do without 沒有……也行
6. do away with 廢除；除去；擺脫
7. put off 拖延；延遲
8. in time 及時；來得及
9. on schedule 按照預定時間；準時
10. hold over 延長；延期

Lesson 30 犯罪 Crimes

1. hold up 持槍搶劫
2. break into 闖入；侵入
3. blow up 爆炸
4. set fire to 放火；焚燒
5. burn down 燒毀
6. let go (of) 放開；釋放
7. tear up 撕裂；撕毀
8. put out 熄滅；使不省人事
9. put down 放下；鎮壓
10. get even with 報復

國家圖書館出版品預行編目資料

一式搞定狄克生片語／Stephen Riter, Steven Tisdale, 李芳田作. —— 初版. —— 臺北市：希伯崙公司，民 95
　面；　公分

ISBN 978-986-7162-46-5（平裝附光碟片）

1. 英國語言 — 成語, 熟語

805.123　　　　　　　　　95018986